Science Notebook

Glencoe Science

Active Reading Note-taking Guide
Science Grade 6

Consultant

Douglas Fisher, Ph.D.

Glencoe

New York, New York   Columbus, Ohio   Chicago, Illinois

About the Consultant

Douglas Fisher, Ph.D., is a Professor in the Department of Teacher Education at San Diego State University. He is the recipient of an International Reading Association Celebrate Literacy Award as well as a Christa McAuliffe award for Excellence in Teacher Education. He has published numerous articles on reading and literacy, differentiated instruction, and curriculum design as well as books, such as *Improving Adolescent Literacy: Strategies at Work* and *Responsive Curriculum Design in Secondary Schools: Meeting the Diverse Needs of Students.* He has taught a variety of courses in SDSU's teacher-credentialing program as well as graduate-level courses on English language development and literacy. He also has taught classes in English, writing, and literacy development to secondary school students.

Send all inquiries to:
Glencoe/McGraw-Hill
8787 Orion Place
Columbus, Ohio 43240-4027

ISBN-13: 978-0-07-879432-2
ISBN-10: 0-07-879432-3

Printed in the United States of America

8 9 10 11   REL 13 12 11 10

Table of Contents

Table of Contents

Your notes are a reminder of what you learned in class. Taking good notes can help you succeed in science. These tips will help you take better notes.

- Be an active listener. Listen for important concepts. Pay attention to words, examples, and/or diagrams your teacher emphasizes.

- Write your notes as clearly and concisely as possible. The following symbols and abbreviations may be helpful in your note-taking.

Word or Phrase	Symbol or Abbreviation	Word or Phrase	Symbol or Abbreviation
for example	e.g.	and	+
such as	i.e.	approximately	≈
with	w/	therefore	∴
without	w/o	versus	vs

- Use a symbol such as a star (★) or an asterisk (*) to emphasis important concepts. Place a question mark (?) next to anything that you do not understand.

- Ask questions and participate in class discussion.

- Draw and label pictures or diagrams to help clarify a concept.

Note-Taking Don'ts

- **Don't** write every word. Concentrate on the main ideas and concepts.

- **Don't** use someone else's notes—they may not make sense.

- **Don't** doodle. It distracts you from listening actively.

- **Don't** lose focus or you will become lost in your note-taking.

Using Your Science Notebook

This note-taking guide is designed to help you succeed in learning science content. Each chapter includes:

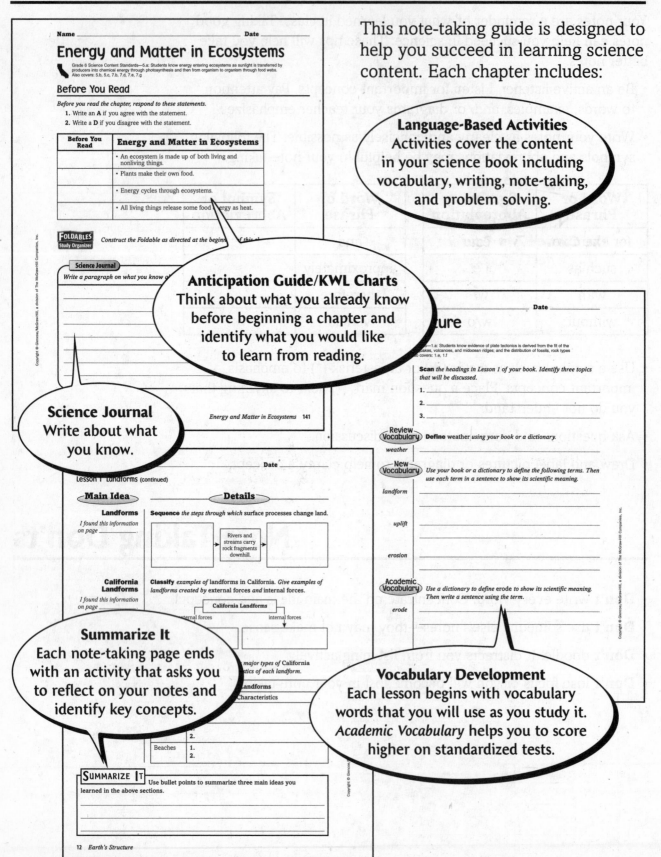

Language-Based Activities
Activities cover the content in your science book including vocabulary, writing, note-taking, and problem solving.

Anticipation Guide/KWL Charts
Think about what you already know before beginning a chapter and identify what you would like to learn from reading.

Science Journal
Write about what you know.

Summarize It
Each note-taking page ends with an activity that asks you to reflect on your notes and identify key concepts.

Vocabulary Development
Each lesson begins with vocabulary words that you will use as you study it. *Academic Vocabulary* helps you to score higher on standardized tests.

Name _____ Date _____

Lesson 4 Earthquake Hazards and Safety (continued)

Main Idea | **Details**

Earthquakes and Structures

I found this information on page _____

Outline *how building planning can help reduce loss of life during an earthquake.*

I. Types of buildings

   A. _____

   _____

   B. _____

II. Earthquake-resistant structures

   A. _____

   B. _____

Earthquake Safety

Model *tips for staying saf... ...ing and after an earthquake. Draw at least two saf...behavio... ...ach environment.*

...tdoors

I found thi...
on...

...esson.

_____

Earthquakes 67

Note-Taking Based on the Cornell Two-Column Format
Practice effective note-taking through the use of graphic organizers, outlines, and written summaries.

Chapter Wrap-Up
This brings the information together for you. Revisiting what you thought at the beginning of the chapter provides another opportunity for you to discuss what you have learned.

Name _____ Date _____

Energy and Matter in Ecosystems
Chapter Wrap-Up

Now that you have read the chapter, think about what you have learned and complete the table below. Compare your previous answers to these.

1. Write an **A** if you agree with the statement.
2. Write a **D** if you disagree with the statement.

Energy and Matter in Ecosystems	After You Read
• An ecosystem is made up of both living and nonliving things.	
• Plants make their own food.	
• Energy cycles through ecosystems.	
• All living things release some food energy as heat.	

Review
Use this checklist to help you study.

☐ Review the information you included in your Foldable.
☐ Study your *Science Notebook* on this chapte...
☐ Study the definitions of vocabulary words.
☐ Review daily homework assignments.
☐ Re-read the chapter and review the cha...
☐ Review the Standards Check at...
☐ Look over the Standards R...

SUMMARIZE IT
each lesson to explain the...

152 Energy and Matter in Ecosystems

Review Checklist
This list helps you assess what you have learned and prepare for your chapter tests.

Name _____ Date _____

Lesson 2 Energy Transfer (continued)

Main Idea | **Details**

Energy Conversions

I found this information on page _____

Label *the diagram of a thrown ball. Use the numbers 1, 2, and 3 to match the statements below.*

1. most potential energy
2. kinetic energy changing into potential energy
3. potential energy changing into kinetic energy

I found this information on page _____

Summarize *how energy changes when a log burns.*

When a log burns, stored _____ is changed

into _____ and _____

Model *how friction changes energy. Complete the flowchart to show how the brakes of a bicycle use friction to stop the bicycle.*

| 1. The bicycle's wheels have kinetic energy. | → | 2. |
| 3. | → | 4. |

SUMMARIZE IT Summarize three main ideas you learned from the above sections.

_____

Thermal Energy and Heat 27

Graphic Organizers
A variety of visual organizers help you to analyze and summarize information and remember content.

Name _____ **Date** _____

Mapping Earth's Surface

Grade 6 Science Content Standards—7.f: Read a topographic map and a geologic map for evidence provided on the maps and construct and interpret a simple scale map. Also covers: 7.b, 7.c, 7.h

Before You Read

Before you read the chapter, think about what you know about the topic. List three things that you already know about mapping Earth's surface in the first column. Then list three things that you would like to learn about the topic in the second column.

K What I know	W What I want to find out

 *Construct the Foldable as directed at the beginning of this chapter.*

Science Journal

List some information you might get from maps if you were planning to build a new home.

_____

_____

_____

_____

_____

Name _Eder Rocha_   **Date** _____

Mapping Earth's Surface
Lesson 1 Reading Maps

 Grade 6 Science Content Standards—7.f: Read a topographic map and a geologic map for evidence provided on the maps and construct and interpret a simple scale map.

Scan *Lesson 1 of your book. Predict three topics that will be covered.*

1. _system or location / longitude_

2. _____

3. _map legends_

Review Vocabulary **Define** pole, *using your book or dictionary.*

pole | _either the end or acces of a spear_

New Vocabulary *Write the correct vocabulary term next to its definition.*

longitude | distance measured on Earth's surface east or west of an imaginary line running from pole to pole through the town of Greenwich, England

latitude | distance measured on Earth's surface north or south of the equator

profile view | view of a map drawn parallel to Earth's surface, as if looking down from above; also called a plan view

map view | view of a map drawn perpendicular to Earth's surface; a cross section

prime factor | list of symbols used on a map

Academic Vocabulary *Use your book or a dictionary to define* ratio. *Then use the term in an original sentence to show its scientific meaning.*

ratio | _the ratio of boys and girls boys win_

Lesson 1 Reading Maps (continued)

Main Idea

Understanding Maps

I found this information on page _____.

I found this information on page _____.

I found this information on page _____.

Details

Summarize *the* purpose of maps.

A map shows where things are _____ on earth _____ or in

relationship to _____ one another _____.

Identify *the* Prime Meridian *and the* equator *on the globe below.*
Then label the equator and poles with their degrees of longitude.
Identify the Northern, Southern, Eastern, *and* Western
Hemispheres.

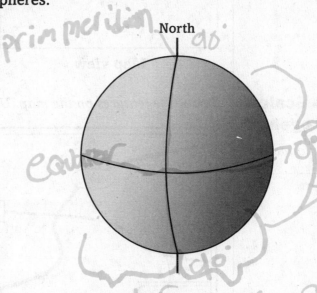

Complete *the diagram to show the relationship between units used*
to measure latitude *and* longitude.

| Earth's circumference is divided into _360_ degrees. | Each degree is divided into _30 min_ | Each _min_ is divided into _60 min_ _sec_ |

SUMMARIZE IT

Summarize the main ideas of this section in three bullets.

· Maps show where objects are on Earth

· The equator divids the Earth into equbys

· For presitian degrees are dvided

Lesson 1 Reading Maps (continued)

Main Idea

Details

Understanding Maps

I found this information on page _____.

Compare *a map view and a* profile view. *Choose an object. Then sketch it in each view.*

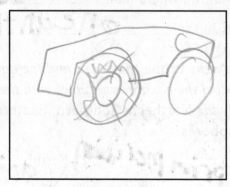

Map view

Profile view

Map Scales and Legends

I found this information on page _____.

CA F P.5

Label *the features on the map. Use the legend.*

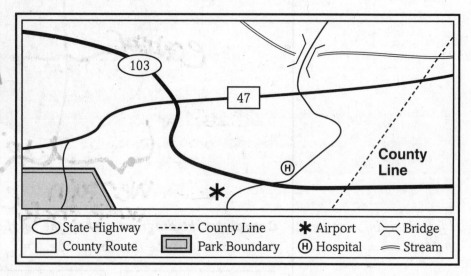

I found this information on page _____.

Rephrase *what is meant by a* map scale *with a ratio of 1:1000.*

A map scole of 1:000 point-
ing

SUMMARIZE IT

Summarize the main ideas of the above sections.

A map veiw of Earths ard even
vow profile veiw shows a sideveiw
veiw a map legent is a vegos on the
ground

Name _____ Date _____

Mapping Earth's Surface
Lesson 2 Topographic Maps and Geologic Maps

 Grade 6 Science Content Standards—7.f: Read a topographic map and a geologic map for evidence provided on the maps and construct and interpret a simple scale map. Also covers: 7.c, 7.h

Scan *the headings and bold words in Lesson 2. Write three questions that come to mind.*

1. what sybols are use For Topograph
2. Hay geolic maps mad
3. What does ageolic cross section show?

Review Vocabulary **Define** geology, *using your book or dictionary.*

geology | study of ears

New Vocabulary *Use your book or a dictionary to define the following terms.*

topographic map | a map used to show the shape of earth

contour line | line drawn on a topographic map to join equil clivation

geologic map | a map to understand geologic maps

geologic formation |

contact | a place where two rocks formation occurs next to eachother

Academic Vocabulary *Use a dictionary to define* interval.

interval | aspace

Lesson 2 Topographic Maps and Geologic Maps (continued)

Main Idea

Details

Topographic Maps

I found this information on page _____.

Distinguish *between* physical *and* cultural features. *Define each type of feature and give examples of each one.*

Feature	Definition	Examples
Physical	made by Nature	mountain valley coastline
Cultural	made by human	pipeline powerline buildings roads

I found this information on page _____.

Model *and label* contour lines *and* contour intervals *by drawing maps of two different hills at the same scale. Show one steep hill and one with a gradually rising slope. Then create topographic profiles of the hills.*

	Steep Slope	Gradual Slope
Contour lines and contour intervals		
Topographic Profile		

SUMMARIZE IT

Summarize the main ideas of the above sections.

Topographic maps show physical and physical features, elevations are contoring or contour intorgurs

Lesson 2 Topographic Maps and Geologic Maps (continued)

Main Idea	**Details**

Geologic Maps

I found this information on page _____ .

Analyze *why understanding an area's geology is important.*
Identify *four ways people use geologic information.*

1. _Predicting likenood of landslide_
2. _determing alability of ground wy_
3. _determing types of soil_
4. _locatehey minralls and roc_

I found this information on page _____ .

Label *the geologic formations and contacts in the cross section below.*

I found this information on page _____ .

Organize *information about two ways in which geologists investigate the geology below Earth's surface.*

Geologists might _they essepss or cliffs_

drill retriver cares

SUMMARIZE IT

Summarize the main ideas of this section in three bullet points.

- _Their are Phar zal reasons for understanding age_
- _pleg. geotic maps shows the rock formations in a area. geologst can shud the underosogy by study exposed rock by drilling_

Mapping Earth's Surface
Chapter Wrap-Up

Review the ideas that you listed in the table at the beginning of the chapter. Cross out any incorrect information in the first column. Then complete the table by filling in the third column.

K What I know	W What I want to find out	L What I learned
The Form o'focks Tell wut year a Tre Fell	about weatuer acedit civilis tion Fossils	you camel if a acedit artic F9a Tre rings

Review

Use this checklist to help you study.

- [ ] Review the information you included in your Foldable.
- [x] Study your *Science Notebook* on this chapter.
- [ ] Study the definitions of vocabulary words.
- [x] Review daily homework assignments.
- [ ] Re-read the chapter and review the charts, graphs, and illustrations.
- [x] Review the Standards Check at the end of each lesson.
- [ ] Look over the Standards Review at the end of the chapter.

SUMMARIZE IT After studying the chapter, summarize three of its main points.

map show wout every thing on earth or that relationship to one another that when the grean dig bections of surpace Feeling geolic mapshous Tru underlyingForimation

Earth's Structure

 Grade 6 Science Content Standards—1.a: Students know evidence of plate tectonics is derived from the fit of the continents; the location of earthquakes, volcanoes, and midocean ridges; and the distribution of fossils, rock types and ancient climate zones. Also covers: 1.b, 1.c, 1.e, 1.f, 2.c

Before You Read

Before you read the chapter, think about what you know about the topic. List three things that you already know about Earth's structure in the first column. Then list three things that you would like to learn about Earth's structure in the second column.

K What I know	W What I want to find out

FOLDABLES™
Study Organizer

Construct the Foldable as directed at the beginning of this chapter.

Science Journal

Describe what an auto collision might look like in slow motion.

_____

_____

_____

_____

_____

_____

_____

Earth's Structure

Lesson 1 Landforms

 Grade 6 Science Content Standards—1.a: Students know evidence of plate tectonics is derived from the fit of the continents; the location of earthquakes, volcanoes, and midocean ridges; and the distribution of fossils, rock types and ancient climate zones. Also covers: 1.f, 2.a, 7.c

Scan *the headings in Lesson 1 of your book. Identify three topics that will be discussed.*

1. _different types of landforms_
2. _land forms found in california_
3. _Mountians_

Review Vocabulary

Define weather *using your book or a dictionary.*

weather   _conditions of the atmosphere_

New Vocabulary

Use your book or a dictionary to define the following terms. Then use each term in a sentence to show its scientific meaning.

landform   _feature_

uplift   _any prosses that mowes the me artns ir face_

erosion   _weaving away_

Academic Vocabulary

Use a dictionary to define transport *to show its scientific meaning. Then write a sentence using the term.*

transport   _____

Lesson 1 Landforms (continued)

Main Idea

How do landscapes form?

I found this information on page _____ .

Details

Model *how* forces within Earth *and* forces at Earth's surface *shape landforms. Draw an example of each.*

Landforms

I found this information on page _____ .

Identify *and describe the 3 main types of* landforms. *Complete the concept map.*

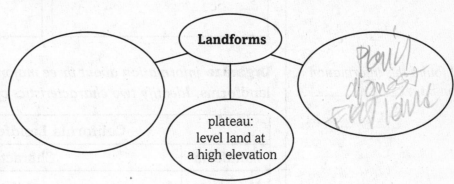

I found this information on page _____ .

Compare and contrast *a mountain and a plateau by completing the table.*

	Mountain	Plateau
Description		
Formed by		

SUMMARIZE IT

Summarize the main ideas of the above sections.

_____

_____

_____

Lesson 1 Landforms (continued)

Main Idea | Details

Landforms

I found this information on page _____.

Sequence *the steps through which* surface processes change land.

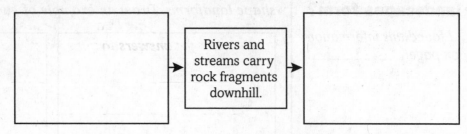

California Landforms

I found this information on page _____.

Classify *examples of* landforms in California. *Give examples of landforms created by* external forces *and* internal forces.

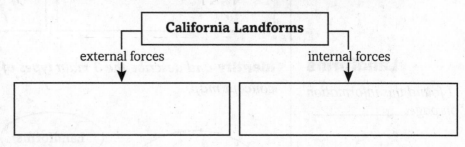

I found this information on page _____.

Organize *information about three major types of* California landforms. *Identify two characteristics of each landform.*

California Landforms	
Landform	Characteristics
Mountains	1. 2.
	1. 2.
Beaches	1. 2.

SUMMARIZE IT Use bullet points to summarize three main ideas you learned in the above sections.

_____

_____

_____

Earth's Structure
Lesson 2 Minerals and Rocks

 Grade 6 Science Content Standards—2.c: Students know beaches are dynamic systems in which the sand is supplied by rivers and moved along the coast by the action of waves. Also covers: 6.b, 6.c, 7.e

Skim *Lesson 2 of your book. Write three questions that come to mind. Look for answers to your questions as you read the section.*

1. _____

2. _____

3. _____

Review Vocabulary **Define** igneous rock, *using your book or dictionary.*

igneous rock _____

New Vocabulary *Use your book or a dictionary to define the following terms.*

minerals little portraits in crystals
_____

density _____

rock The partn of the on cleg

magma dried lavel

lava melted crystls and conts

sediment soil ignivos Rock in layers ok

rock cycle _____

Academic Vocabulary *Use a dictionary to define* appreciate. *Then use the term in a sentence to show its scientific meaning.*

appreciate _____

Lesson 2 Minerals and Rocks (continued)

Main Idea

Details

What is Earth made of?

I found this information on page _____.

Identify *five* characteristics of minerals.

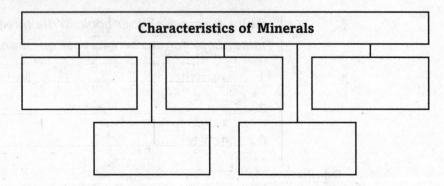

Characteristics of Minerals

I found this information on page _____.

Organize *the following substances on the* Mohs Hardness Scale.

diamond   gypsum   quartz   talc   topaz

Softest								Hardest	
1	2	3	4	5	6	7	8	9	10

Physical Properties of Minerals

I found this information on page _____.

Create *a concept map that lists the* physical properties *that can be used to identify minerals.*

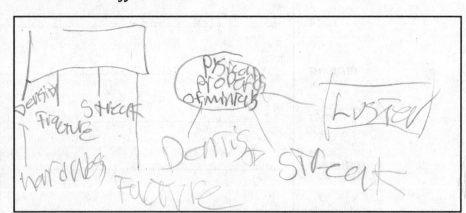

SUMMARIZE IT

Summarize the main ideas of the above sections.

_____

_____

_____

Name _____   **Date** _____

Lesson 2 Minerals and Rocks (continued)

Main Idea	Details

Mineral Uses

I found this information on page _____.

Complete *the table to summarize the uses of the* metallic ores *shown.*

Metallic Ore	Metal	Used In
Chalcopyrite, malachite		
Hematite, magnetite		
Galena		

Rocks

I found this information on page _____.

Identify *the 3 major* groups of rocks.

1. _____   2. _____   3. _____

Compare and contrast granite *and* basalt. *Place all of the words or phrases below in the Venn diagram.*

- igneous
- fine-grained
- cooled quickly
- formed from lava
- coarse-grained
- low-density minerals
- formed from magma
- cooled slowly
- high-density minerals

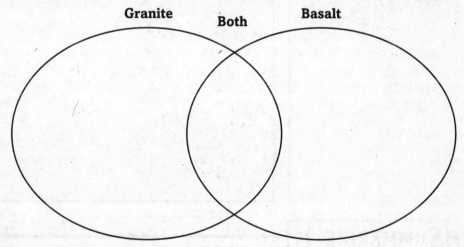

Granite   Both   Basalt

SUMMARIZE IT Write three sentences to summarize the main ideas you learned from the above sections.

_____

_____

Lesson 2 Minerals and Rocks (continued)

Main Idea   Details

*I found this information
on page _____.*

Analyze *the process that forms* **metamorphic rocks.**

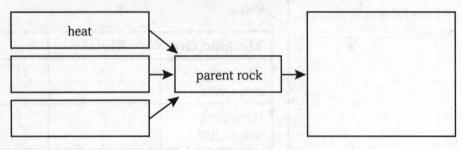

*I found this information
on page _____.*

Sequence *the steps that form* **sedimentary rock.**

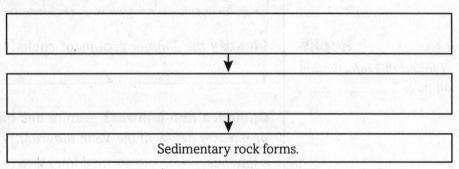

*I found this information
on page _____.*

Design *a diagram showing the* **processes of the rock cycle.**

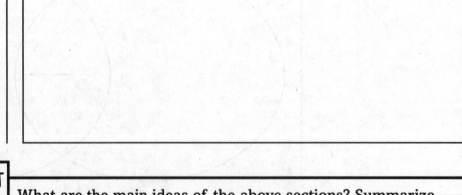

SUMMARIZE IT
**What are the main ideas of the above sections? Summarize
these ideas in your own words.**

_____

_____

_____

Earth's Structure
Lesson 3 Earth's Interior

 Grade 6 Science Content Standards—1.b: Students know Earth is composed of several layers: a cold, brittle lithosphere; a hot, convecting mantle; and a dense, metallic core. Also covers: 4.c, 7.e, 7.g

Scan *the* What You'll Learn *statements for Lesson 3 of your book. Predict three topics that will be discussed.*

1. _____

2. _____

3. _____

Review Vocabulary **Define** magnetic field *using your book or a dictionary.*

magnetic field _____

_____

New Vocabulary *Use your book or a dictionary to define the following terms.*

crust _____

_____

mantle _____

_____

asthenosphere _____

_____

core _____

_____

lithosphere _____

Academic Vocabulary *Use a dictionary to define* layer. *Then use the term in a scientific sentence.*

layer _____

Lesson 3 Earth's Interior (continued)

Main Idea

Details

Layers

I found this information on page _____ .

Model *how* heat *and* pressure *change inside Earth. Draw an arrow to show how heat and pressure increase.*

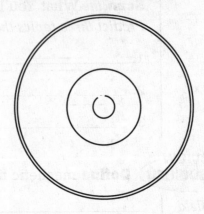

I found this information on page _____ .

Organize *information about the 3 major* layers *of Earth in the table below. List at least four characteristics for each layer.*

Earth's Major Layers	Characteristics
Crust	
Mantle	
Core	

SUMMARIZE IT

Highlight the main idea of this section below.

Though scientists cannot see the inside of Earth directly, they use earthquake waves to study it. They have learned that Earth has three major sections: the crust, the mantle, and the core. The lithosphere is made up of the crust and the top part of the mantle.

Lesson 3 Earth's Interior (continued)

Main Idea

Heat Transfer in Earth

I found this information on page _____.

I found this information on page _____.

Details

Label *the arrow with the words below to compare the* density of Earth's layers.

core   crust   mantle

least dense   most dense

→

_____   _____   _____

Summarize *how thermal energy is transferred within Earth.*

_____

_____

_____

Analyze *how* convection *affects other processes on Earth.* *Complete the concept map.*

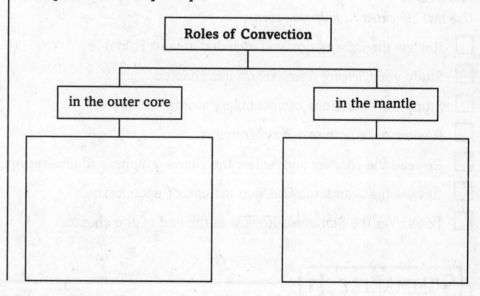

Roles of Convection

in the outer core   in the mantle

SUMMARIZE IT

Summarize three main ideas from the above sections using bullet points.

_____

_____

_____

Earth's Structure Chapter Wrap-Up

Review the ideas you listed in the table at the beginning of the chapter. Cross out any incorrect information in the first column. Then complete the table by filling in the third column.

K What I know	W What I want to find out	L What I learned

Review

Use this checklist to help you study.

- ☐ Review the information you included in your Foldable.
- ☐ Study your *Science Notebook* on this chapter.
- ☐ Study the definitions of vocabulary words.
- ☐ Review daily homework assignments.
- ☐ Re-read the chapter and review the charts, graphs, and illustrations.
- ☐ Review the Standards Check at the end of each lesson.
- ☐ Look over the Standards Review at the end of the chapter.

SUMMARIZE IT After studying the chapter, write one sentence summarizing the main idea of each lesson.

_____

_____

_____

_____

Thermal Energy and Heat

Grade 6 Science Content Standards—3.a: Students know energy can be carried from one place to another by heat flow or by waves, including water, light and sound waves, or by moving objects. Also covers: 3.b, 3.c, 3.d, 7.a, 7.c

Before You Read

Before you read the chapter, think about what you know about the topic. List three things that you already know about thermal energy and heat in the first column. Then list three things that you would like to learn about these topics in the second column.

K What I know	W What I want to find out

Construct the Foldable as directed at the beginning of this chapter.

Science Journal

List three changes that occur when you light a match.

_____

_____

_____

_____

_____

_____

Thermal Energy and Heat
Lesson 1 Forms of Energy

Grade 6 Science Content Standards—3.a: Students know energy can be carried from one place to another by heat flow or by waves, including water, light and sound waves, or by moving objects.

Scan *Lesson 1 of your book. Write two facts you discovered about forms of energy while scanning the lesson.*

1. _____

2. _____

Review Vocabulary

Define gravity, *using your book or dictionary.*

gravity

_____

_____

_____

New Vocabulary

Use your book or a dictionary to define the following terms.

energy

_____

_____

kinetic energy

_____

_____

potential energy

_____

_____

elastic potential energy

_____

_____

thermal energy

_____

_____

Academic Vocabulary

Use a dictionary to find the scientific definition of the term occur. *Then write an original scientific sentence using the term.*

occur   _____

Lesson 1 Forms of Energy (continued)

⊂ **Main Idea** ⊃ _____ ⊂ **Details** ⊃

What is energy?

I found this information on page _____.

Define energy, *and give an example of energy from your everyday life.*

Energy is _____.

Example: _____

I found this information on page _____.

Analyze *the relationship between* kinetic energy, speed, *and* mass. *Draw arrows to show how kinetic energy changes as mass and speed change.*

mass ⟶

kinetic energy

speed ⟶

kinetic energy

Identify *the unit used to measure energy.*

Energy is measured in _____. The symbol for this

unit is _____.

Potential Energy— Stored Energy

I found this information on page _____.

Distinguish *two ways to increase the gravitational potential energy of an object.*

To increase gravitational potential energy	→	
	or	

┌─ **SUMMARIZE IT** ─────────────────────────────────────┐

Write three main ideas from these sections.

_____

_____

_____
└──┘

Thermal Energy and Heat **23**

Lesson 1 Forms of Energy (continued)

Main Idea   **Details**

Potential Energy—Stored Energy

I found this information on page _____.

Model *and label two ways a spring can store* elastic potential energy.

A spring can store elastic potential energy when it is _____

or _____.

Contrast *the ways* chemical potential energy *is stored and released.*

Chemical energy is stored in _____ _____.	Chemical energy is released when _____ _____.

Light Energy and Thermal Energy

I found this information on page _____.

Complete *the table to describe* light energy *and* thermal energy.

Form of Energy	Definition	Characteristics
Light energy		
Thermal energy		

SUMMARIZE IT
Write 4 sentences to summarize the main ideas of these sections.

_____

_____

_____

Thermal Energy and Heat
Lesson 2 Energy Transfer

 Grade 6 Science Content Standards—3.a: Students know energy can be carried from one place to another by heat flow or by waves, including water, light and sound waves, or by moving objects. Also covers: 3.b

Skim *Lesson 2, and predict two topics that will be covered in this lesson.*

1. _____

_____

2. _____

_____

Review Vocabulary   **Define** force. *Use a dictionary or your book for help.*

force   _____

New Vocabulary   *Use your book or a dictionary to define each term.*

work   _____

_____

wave   _____

_____

fuel   _____

_____

friction   _____

_____

Academic Vocabulary   *Use a dictionary to define the term* transfer *as it is used in the following sentence.*

Like all waves, water waves transfer kinetic energy from one place to another.

transfer   _____

Lesson 2 Energy Transfer (continued)

Main Idea | Details

Moving Objects Transfer Energy

I found this information on page _____.

Identify *the characteristics of work. Complete the concept map.*

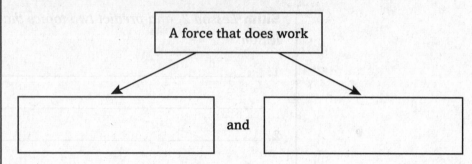

A force that does work

and

Waves Transfer Energy

I found this information on page _____.

Model *how waves carry energy. Draw a water wave and a sound wave. Use arrows to show how matter and energy move.*

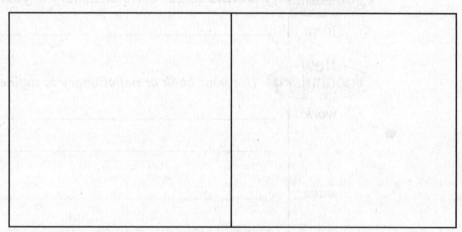

I found this information on page _____.

Contrast electromagnetic waves *with water and sound waves.* *Then list five types of electromagnetic wave.*

_____

_____

_____

SUMMARIZE IT

Summarize three main ideas from the above section.

_____

_____

_____

_____

Lesson 2 Energy Transfer (continued)

Main Idea

Energy Conversions

I found this information on page _____.

I found this information on page _____.

Details

Label *the diagram of a thrown ball. Use the numbers 1, 2, and 3 to match the statements below.*

1. most potential energy

2. kinetic energy changing into potential energy

3. potential energy changing into kinetic energy

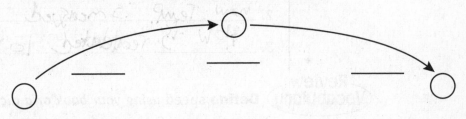

Summarize *how energy changes when a log burns.*

When a log burns, stored _____ is changed

into _____ and _____.

Model *how* friction *changes energy. Complete the flowchart to show how the brakes of a bicycle use friction to stop the bicycle.*

1. The bicycle's wheels have kinetic energy.	**2.**
3.	**4.**

SUMMARIZE IT

Summarize three main ideas you learned from the above sections.

_____

_____

_____

Name _____ Date _____

Thermal Energy and Heat
Lesson 3 Temperature, Thermal Energy, and Heat

Grade 6 Science Content Standards—3.a: Students know energy can be carried from one place to another by heat flow or by waves, including water, light and sound waves, or by moving objects. Also covers: 7.c

Predict *three things you will learn in this lesson. Use the headings to help you.*

1. _what Temp is_
2. _how Temp. is measured_
3. _HOW is realdated to Temp_

Review Vocabulary

Define speed *using your book or a dictionary.*

speed _measure of how quickly_

New Vocabulary

Use your book or a dictionary to define the following terms.

temperature _measure of the averge Keintk energy) when the Temp_

thermal expansion _____

heat _____

Academic Vocabulary

Use a dictionary to write the scientific definition for volume. *Then write a sentence from this lesson in which the term appears.*

volume Definition: _____

Sentence: _____

Name _____ cher _____ Date _____

Lesson 3 Temperature, Thermal Energy, and Heat (continued)

Main Idea	Details

What is temperature?

I found this information on page _____.

skip ⟶

Create *a diagram to show the relationship between* temperature, kinetic energy, *and the* motion of the particles *in an object.*

Cooler	Warmer

I found this information on page _____.

Sequence *the steps that cause* thermal expansion *when a balloon is heated with a hair dryer. Complete the flowchart.*

hair drier warms particles in the room

↓

As temp increases, air particles move faster when air particles

↓

Air particles tend to move farther apart

↓

The air in the balloon expands

SUMMARIZE IT

In your own words, summarize the main ideas of this section.

When particles inc motived move faster. When they have ke int energy. When Avege of particles increases the temp of the motived expands the temp increases

Lesson 3 Temperature, Thermal Energy, and Heat (continued)

Main Idea	Details

Measuring Temperature

I found this information on page _____.

Compare *the* Fahrenheit, Celsius, *and* Kelvin temperature scales. *Complete the table.*

	Fahrenheit	**Celsius**	**Kelvin**
Water boils	2 12°	100°	373
Water freezes	82°	0°	273°

Heat

I found this information on page _____.

Sequence *the* process of heat flow *between a bowl of hot soup and the surrounding air. Complete the flowchart.*

A bowl of soup is warmer than the air around it.

↓

Thermal energy flows from soup to the air.

↓

Particles in the air move faster and the particles move slowly.

↓

The temp of the air increases and the temp of the soup

↓

The soup and the air reach the same temperature.

SUMMARIZE IT

Rephrase three main ideas of the above sections in your own words.

three common temp scales. heat always transfer energy from something at a lower temp than itself,

Name _____   Date _____

Thermal Energy and Heat
Lesson 4 Conduction, Convection, and Radiation

 Grade 6 Science Content Standards—3.c: Students know heat flows in solids by conduction (which involves no flow of matter) and in fluids by conduction and by convection (which involves flow of matter). Also covers: 3.d, 7.a

Scan *Lesson 4. Write three facts that you discovered as you scanned the lesson.*

1. _____

   _____

2. _____

   _____

3. _____

   _____

Review Vocabulary   **Define** density, *using your book or dictionary.*

density   _____

New Vocabulary   *Write the term that matches each definition.*

_____fluid_____   material made of particles that can easily change locations

_____conduction_____   transfer of heat by collisions between particles in matter

_____radiation_____   transfer of thermal energy by electromagnetic waves

_____convection_____   transfer of thermal energy by the movement of matter from one place to another

_____conductor_____   material in which thermal energy moves quickly

_____convection current_____   overall movement of water

Academic Vocabulary   *Use a dictionary to write the definition for* summary. *Then write a sentence using the term.*

summary   _____

   _____

Lesson 4 Conduction, Convection, and Radiation (continued)

Main Idea

Details

Conduction

*I found this information
on page _____.*

Model *how energy moves between particles in* conduction. *Use arrows to show the transfer of energy.*

*I found this information
on page _____.*

Contrast conductors *and* insulators. *Complete the table.*

	Conductors	**Insulators**
Speed of conduction		
Examples		

Convection

*I found this information
on page _____.*

Analyze *the transfer of energy by* convection.

In convection, thermal energy is transferred by _____ _____. In fluids, the particles _____. In solids, the particles _____.

SUMMARIZE IT

After reading the above sections, summarize the main ideas.

_____

_____

_____

_____

Name _____ **Date** _____

Lesson 4 Conduction, Convection, and Radiation (continued)

Main Idea

Details

I found this information on page _____.

Summarize *how* changes in temperature and density *cause a hot-air balloon to rise. Complete the flow chart.*

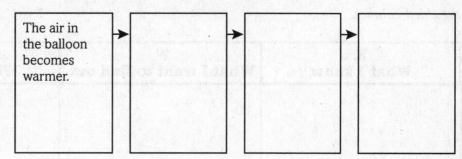

| The air in the balloon becomes warmer. | → | | → | | → | |

I found this information on page _____.

Model *how* convection currents form *by drawing a diagram.*

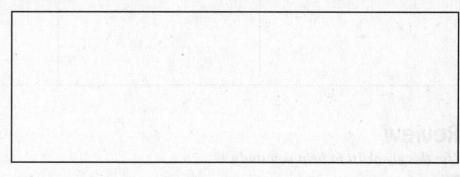

Radiation

I found this information on page _____.

Organize *information about* radiation. *Complete the concept map.*

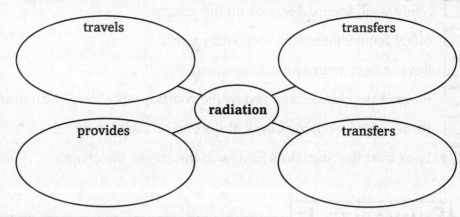

travels   transfers

radiation

provides   transfers

SUMMARIZE IT

Summarize two main ideas from the above sections.

_____

_____

_____

Name _____ Date _____

Thermal Energy and Heat
Chapter Wrap-Up

Review the ideas you listed in the table at the beginning of the chapter. Cross out any incorrect information in the first column. Then complete the table by filling in the third column.

K What I know	W What I want to find out	L What I learned

Review

Use this checklist to help you study.

- ☐ Review the information you included in your Foldable.
- ☐ Study your *Science Notebook* on this chapter.
- ☐ Study the definitions of vocabulary words.
- ☐ Review daily homework assignments.
- ☐ Re-read the chapter and review the charts, graphs, and illustrations.
- ☐ Review the Standards Check at the end of each lesson.
- ☐ Look over the Standards Review at the end of the chapter.

SUMMARIZE IT
After reading this chapter, write three main ideas that you learned about thermal energy and heat.

_____

_____

_____

Plate Tectonics

Grade 6 Science Content Standards—1.a: Students know evidence of plate tectonics is derived from the fit of the continents; the location of earthquakes, volcanoes, and midocean ridges; and the distribution of fossils, rock types, and ancient climatic zones. Also covers: 1.b, 1.c, 4.c, 7.a, 7.e, 7.g

Before You Read

Before you read the chapter, respond to these statements.

    1. Write an **A** if you agree with the statement.

    2. Write a **D** if you disagree with the statement.

Before You Read	Plate Tectonics
	• Fossil evidence supports the idea that continents have moved over time.
	• New seafloor forms as lava flows through cracks in ocean floors.
	• Earth's crust is broken into sections called plates.
	• Earth's plates do not move.

Construct the Foldable as directed at the beginning of this chapter.

Science Journal

Write three questions you would ask a geologist about plate tectonics.

_____

_____

_____

_____

_____

_____

Plate Tectonics
Lesson 1 Continental Drift

 Grade 6 Science Content Standards—1.a: Students know evidence of plate tectonics is derived from the fit of the continents; the location of earthquakes, volcanoes, and midocean ridges; and the distribution of fossils, rock types, and ancient climatic zones. Also covers: 7.e

Skim *Lesson 1 of your book. Write three questions that come to mind from reading the headings and examining the illustrations. Look for the answers as you read.*

1. _What continents were_____

2. _~~did~~ movments like_____

3. _____

Review Vocabulary

Define rock *using your book or a dictionary.*

rock

anature solid mixture of mineral crystal partials

New Vocabulary

Use your book to define the following terms. Then write an original sentence for each term.

continental drift

The 'scas of the continents drifting away from each other and formed one super continent

Pangaea

a super continent w

Academic Vocabulary

Use a dictionary to define data. *Then use the term in a sentence to show its meaning.*

data _____

_____

_____

Lesson 1 Continental Drift (continued)

Main Idea

Drifting Continents

I found this information on page _____ .

Details

Rephrase Alfred Wegener's hypothesis *about Earth's continents in your own words.*

brilliant and I Never thought it would

_____

_____

_____

Model *what* Pangaea *looked like. Draw a map showing the connected continents.*

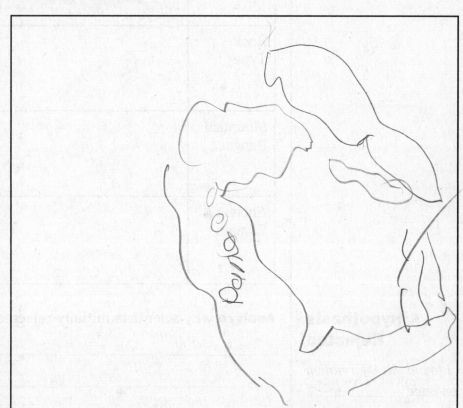

SUMMARIZE IT Highlight the main idea of this section of the lesson below.

In the early 1900s, Alfred Wegener proposed a hypothesis to explain why the edges of the continents looked as though they could fit together like pieces of a jigsaw puzzle. Wegener thought that millions of years ago, all of the continents had formed one large landmass called Pangaea. Wegener hypothesized that Pangaea broke apart and the continents slowly drifted to their current locations.

Lesson 1 Continental Drift (continued)

Main Idea

Details

Evidence for Continental Drift

I found this information on page 168-171

Organize *information about the* evidence for continental drift. *Complete the table.*

Evidence	Description
Fit of Continents	The edges of the continents fit together. South america, Africa u.s. europe etc.
Fossils	certain plants and animals are found in the same organisms found when broken up all
Rock Types	
Mountain Ranges	
Ancient Climate	

A Hypothesis Rejected

I found this information on page P172.

Analyze why scientists initially rejected Wegener's hypothesis.

since test did not exert mass

_____

_____

SUMMARIZE IT

Summarize two main ideas of the above sections.

_____

_____

_____

Plate Tectonics
Lesson 2 Seafloor Spreading

 Grade 6 Science Content Standards—1.a: Students know evidence of plate tectonics is derived from the fit of the continents; the location of earthquakes, volcanoes, and midocean ridges; and the distribution of fossils, rock types, and ancient climatic zones. Also covers: 7.g

Predict *three topics that might be discussed in Lesson 2 after reading its headings.*

1. _____

2. _____

3. _____

Review Vocabulary

Define magma *using your book or a dictionary.*

magma _____
_____

New Vocabulary

Use your book to define each vocabulary term. Then write one sentence that shows how the terms are related.

mid-ocean ridge _____
_____

seafloor spreading _____
_____

Sentence: _____
_____

Academic Vocabulary

Use a dictionary to define hypothesis.

hypothesis _____
_____

Lesson 2 Seafloor Spreading (continued)

Main Idea

Details

Investigating the Seafloor

I found this information on page _____.

Summarize *discoveries that scientists have made from studying the seafloor.*

_____

_____

_____

The Seafloor Moves

I found this information on page _____.

Model *the process of* seafloor spreading. *Draw a cross section of a mid-ocean ridge and the magma below it. Use arrows to indicate the directions of motion.*

Evidence for Spreading

I found this information on page _____.

Identify *the position of Earth's magnetic poles today and when they are reversed.*

Normal

Reversed

SUMMARIZE IT

Summarize the two main ideas of the above sections with two bullet points.

_____

_____

_____

Lesson 2 Seafloor Spreading (continued)

Main Idea

Evidence for Spreading

I found this information on page _____ .

I found this information on page _____ .

Details

Label *the diagram below to show what scientists learned from studying* magnetic reversals. *Add arrows to show the direction of spreading, and indicate where older rock and newer rock occur.*

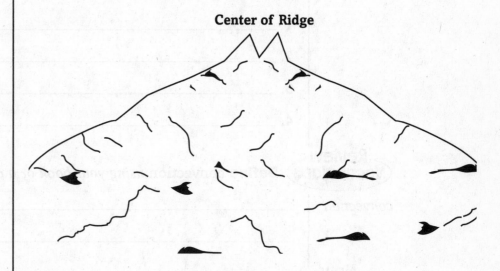

Center of Ridge

Organize *information about how scientists have used seafloor drilling to provide evidence for seafloor spreading.*

   I. Methods

       A. _____

       B. _____

   II. Results

       A. _____

       B. _____

SUMMARIZE IT

Highlight the main idea of this section below.

Scientists use information from Earth's magnetic pole reversals to determine the age of basalt rock on the seafloor. This has provided evidence for seafloor spreading. The youngest rock is found closest to mid-ocean ridges, and the oldest rock is found farthest away.

Plate Tectonics
Lesson 3 Theory of Plate Tectonics

 Grade 6 Science Content Standards—1.b: Students know Earth is composed of several layers: a cold, brittle lithosphere; a hot, convecting mantle; and a dense, metallic core. Also covers: 1.c, 4.c

Scan *the headings in Lesson 3 of your book. Identify four topics that will be discussed.*

1. _____

2. _____

3. _____

4. _____

Review Vocabulary

convection

Define convection *using your book or a dictionary.*

_____

_____

New Vocabulary

Use your book or a dictionary to define each vocabulary term.

lithospheric plate

_____

_____

plate tectonics

_____

_____

ocean trench

_____

_____

slab

_____

_____

Academic Vocabulary

define

Use a dictionary to define define. *Then use the term in a sentence to show its scientific meaning.*

_____

_____

Lesson 3 Theory of Plate Tectonics (continued)

Main Idea — **Details**

Earth's Plates

I found this information on page _____.

Organize *evidence for* plate boundaries *on Earth.*

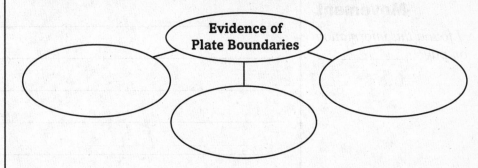

Types of Lithosphere

I found this information on page _____.

Identify *and describe the two different* types of lithosphere.

Types of lithosphere ⟨ _____
_____

What controls plate movement?

I found this information on page _____.

Summarize *how forces within Earth affect plates.*

Type of Force	Effect
Convection	
Ridge Push	
Slab Pull	

SUMMARIZE IT

Summarize two main ideas of the above sections.

_____
_____
_____

Lesson 3 Theory of Plate Tectonics (continued)

Main Idea

Details

Measuring Plate Movement

I found this information on page _____.

Explain *how satellites are used to measure the movement of plates.*

_____

_____

_____

_____

_____

Plate Tectonics and the Rock Cycle

I found this information on page _____.

Create *a diagram showing how plate tectonics moves materials through the rock cycle.*

SUMMARIZE IT

Summarize three main ideas of the above sections.

_____

_____

_____

Tie It Together

Synthesize It

Your book has a picture showing how continents may have drifted. It shows their positions 250 million years ago, 125 million years ago, and at the present. Work with a partner to trace the paths that the continents have taken. Then extend their paths forward in time to project where they may be 125 million years from now. Draw a map in the space below, showing your prediction. Present your prediction to the class.

Plate Tectonics Chapter Wrap-Up

Now that you have read the chapter, think about what you have learned and complete the table below. Compare your previous answers to these.

1. Write an **A** if you agree with the statement.
2. Write a **D** if you disagree with the statement.

Plate Tectonics	After You Read
• Fossil evidence supports the idea that continents have moved over time.	
• New seafloor forms as lava flows through cracks in ocean floors.	
• Earth's crust is broken into sections called plates.	
• Earth's plates do not move.	

Review

Use this checklist to help you study.

☐ Review the information you included in your Foldable.

☐ Study your *Science Notebook* on this chapter.

☐ Study the definitions of vocabulary words.

☐ Review daily homework assignments.

☐ Re-read the chapter and review the charts, graphs, and illustrations.

☐ Review the Standards Check at the end of each lesson.

☐ Look over the Standards Review at the end of the chapter.

SUMMARIZE IT
After studying the chapter, write one sentence to summarize the main idea of each lesson.

_____

_____

_____

_____

Plate Boundaries and California

Grade 6 Science Content Standards—1.f: Students know how to explain major features of California geology (including mountains, faults, volcanoes) in terms of plate tectonics. Also covers: 1.c–e, 7.a–b, 7.e, 7.g

Before You Read

Before you read the chapter, respond to these statements.

   1. Write an **A** if you agree with the statement.

   2. Write a **D** if you disagree with the statement.

Before You Read	Plate Boundaries and California
	• Plates in Earth's crust can move only from side to side.
	• Many of California's mountains formed as the result of plate movements.
	• All of California is located on the same lithospheric plate.
	• Los Angeles and San Francisco are slowly moving toward each other.

Construct the Foldable as directed at the beginning of this chapter.

Science Journal

You are an explorer and it is 1776. Write your description of the Sierra Nevada and your thoughts as you view these mountains for the first time.

_____

_____

_____

_____

_____

_____

Plate Boundaries and California
Lesson 1 Interactions at Plate Boundaries

Grade 6 Science Content Standards—1.c: Students know lithospheric plates the size of continents and oceans move at rates of centimeters per year in response to movements in the mantle. Also covers: 1.d, 1.e, 7.g

Skim *Lesson 1. Look at the section headings and illustrations.*
Write three topics that you predict will be covered in the lesson.

1. _____

2. _____

3. _____

Review Vocabulary **Define** lithospheric plate *using your book or a dictionary.*

lithospheric plate _____

New Vocabulary *Match the correct term with its definition.*

_____ long, narrow valley formed as the hanging wall of a divergent boundary slips down

_____ fracture in which rocks on one side of the fracture move relative to rocks on the other side

_____ boundary formed when two plates move apart

_____ boundary formed when two plates move sideways past each other

_____ break or crack in rock

_____ process that pulls apart a continent

_____ boundary formed when two plates move toward each other

Academic Vocabulary *Use your book or a dictionary to define* inclined.

inclined _____

_____

_____

_____

Lesson 1 Interactions at Plate Boundaries (continued)

Main Idea

Details

Stress and Deformation

I found this information on page _____.

Organize *information about* types of stress. *Describe how each type of stress occurs and its results.*

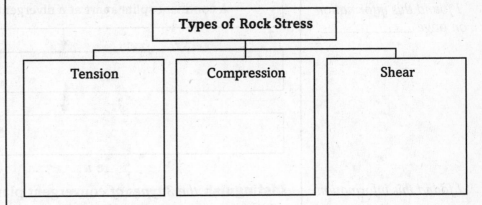

I found this information on page _____.

Model *the 3 main types of* faults. *Draw each type of fault, and label the* hanging wall *and* footwall. *Use arrows to show how rock moves.*

Normal Fault	Reverse Fault	Strike-Slip Fault

SUMMARIZE IT Rephrase the main ideas of this section in your own words.

_____

_____

_____

_____

Lesson 1 Interactions at Plate Boundaries (continued)

Main Idea

Details

Types of Plate Boundaries

I found this information on page _____ .

Sequence *the events that occur during* continental rifting.

A continent splits apart at a divergent plate boundary.

↓

↓

I found this information on page _____ .

Distinguish *the 3 types of* convergent plate boundaries. *Describe what happens at each type of boundary.*

Ocean-to-Ocean	Ocean-to-Continent	Continent-to-Continent

I found this information on page _____ .

Complete *this paragraph about* transform plate boundaries.

At transform plate boundaries, plates _____

_____ . In the ocean, these boundaries connect _____

_____ . On the continents, _____

_____ can occur along these boundaries.

SUMMARIZE IT

Summarize three main ideas from the above section of Lesson 1.

_____

_____

_____

Plate Boundaries and California
Lesson 2 California Geology

 Grade 6 Science Content Standards—1.f: Students know how to explain major features of California geology (including mountains, faults, volcanoes) in terms of plate tectonics. Also covers: 1.e, 7.a, 7.b

Scan *the headings and bold words in Lesson 2. Write three questions that come to mind. Look for answers as you read.*

1. _____

2. _____

3. _____

Review Vocabulary

Define uplift *using your book or a dictionary.*

uplift

_____

_____

New Vocabulary

Use your book or a dictionary to define San Andreas Fault. *Then write a short paragraph that describes the fault.*

San Andreas Fault

_____

_____

_____

_____

_____

_____

_____

_____

_____

_____

Academic Vocabulary

Use a dictionary to define adjacent. *Then use the term in an original sentence related to Lesson 2.*

adjacent

_____

_____

Lesson 2 California Geology (continued)

⟨ **Main Idea** ⟩ —————————— ⟨ **Details** ⟩

Plate Tectonics in California

I found this information on page _____.

Distinguish *two plate boundaries found in California.*

1. _____
   _____

2. _____
   _____

Identify *three features of California geology caused by plate tectonics.*

1. _____   2. _____   3. _____

I found this information on page _____.

Create *a diagram showing the* **San Andreas Fault.** *Use the words below to label your diagram. Include arrows to show how the plates are moving.*

- North American Plate
- Pacific Plate
- San Francisco Bay
- transverse ranges
- coast ranges
- Salton Sea
- Los Angeles Basin
- Ventura Basin
- Cape Mendocino

[diagram box]

⟨ SUMMARIZE IT ⟩

Summarize the main ideas of the above section of the lesson.

_____
_____
_____

Lesson 2 California Geology (continued)

Main Idea

Details

I found this information on page _____.

Analyze *the role of a convergent plate boundary in shaping California geology. Complete the cause-and-effect diagram.*

| The Gorda and Juan de Fuca plates are forced beneath the coast. | → | |

California's Mountains

I found this information on page _____.

Organize *information about the formation of mountains in California. Complete the outline.*

I. Subduction

   A. _____

      _____

   B. _____

      _____

II. Rifting

   A. _____

   B. _____

Future Plate Movements

I found this information on page _____.

Summarize *two changes that might occur in the future as a result of plate tectonics.*

_____

_____

_____

_____

SUMMARIZE IT

Rephrase the main ideas of the lesson in your own words.

_____

_____

_____

Plate Boundaries and California
Chapter Wrap-Up

Now that you have read the chapter, think about what you have learned and complete the table below. Compare your previous answers to these.

1. Write an **A** if you agree with the statement.
2. Write a **D** if you disagree with the statement.

Plate Boundaries and California	After You Read
• Plates in Earth's crust can move only from side to side.	
• Many of California's mountains formed as the result of plate movements.	
• All of California is located on the same lithospheric plate.	
• Los Angeles and San Francisco are slowly moving toward each other.	

Review
Use this checklist to help you study.

☐ Review the information you included in your Foldable.

☐ Study your *Science Notebook* on this chapter.

☐ Study the definitions of vocabulary words.

☐ Review daily homework assignments.

☐ Re-read the chapter and review the charts, graphs, and illustrations.

☐ Review the Standards Check at the end of each lesson.

☐ Look over the Standards Review at the end of the chapter.

SUMMARIZE IT After studying this chapter, write sentences summarizing three of its main ideas.

_____

_____

_____

_____

Earthquakes

Grade 6 Science Content Standards—1.g: Students know how to determine the epicenter of an earthquake and know that the effects of an earthquake on any region vary, depending on the size of the earthquake, the distance of the region from the epicenter, the local geology, and the type of construction in the region. Also covers: 1.d, 1.e, 2.d, 7.a–b, 7.d–e, 7.g

Before You Read

Before you read the chapter, respond to these statements.

   1. Write an **A** if you agree with the statement.

   2. Write a **D** if you disagree with the statement.

Before You Read	Earthquakes
	• Plate movements cause earthquakes.
	• Scientists use earthquake waves to map the inside of Earth.
	• The Richter scale is the only way to measure the strength of an earthquake.
	• Fire is the most common hazard that occurs following an earthquake.

Construct the Foldable as directed at the beginning of this chapter.

Science Journal

Have you ever experienced an earthquake? If so, write a paragraph about the event. If not, write how you imagine it would feel to experience an earthquake.

_____

_____

_____

_____

_____

_____

_____

Earthquakes

Lesson 1 Origins of Earthquakes

 Grade 6 Science Content Standard—1.d: Students know that earthquakes are sudden motions along breaks in the crust called faults and that volcanoes and fissures are locations where magma reaches the surface. Also covers 1.e, 7.e

Scan *Lesson 1 of your book. Write two important facts you discovered about the origins of earthquakes while scanning the lesson.*

1. _The Yosemit_

2. _____

Review Vocabulary

Define fault *using your book or a dictionary.*

fault _A fracture alongwhich facts on side have Moved relative to facts on the other side_

New Vocabulary

Use your book or a dictionary to define the following terms.

earthquake _a rapture and sudden movements of a fault_

elastic strain _energy stored in change all strength_

focus _Where energy is firs Resist ona earth quack_

Academic Vocabulary

Use a dictionary to find the scientific definition of the term interact. *Find a sentence in the lesson in which the word is used, and write the sentence below.*

interact Definition: _to act on each other_

Sentence: _I interacted with my pencil_

_____

_____

Lesson 1 Origins of Earthquakes (continued)

⬭ **Main Idea**	⬭ **Details**

What is an earthquake?

I found this information on page _____.

Sequence *the* changes in energy *that occur leading up to an earthquake.*

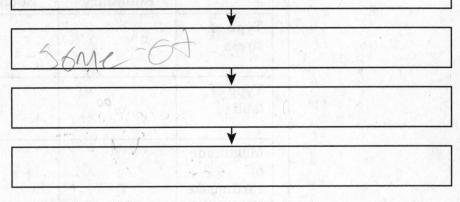

| Heat energy moves through Earth's mantle by convection. |

↓

| Some of |

↓

| |

↓

| |

I found this information on page _____.

Summarize *what happens after* elastic strain *builds up in rocks.* **Complete the statements below.**

When elastic strain builds up, rocks _____

_____. Either _____, or the

rupture will occur _____.

Model *the* spread of seismic waves *from the focus of an earthquake. Use arrows to show how waves spread.*

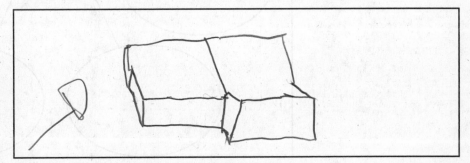

SUMMARIZE IT

Summarize two main ideas of the above sections.

_____

_____

_____

Lesson 1 Origins of Earthquakes (continued)

Main Idea

Plate Boundaries and Earthquakes

I found this information on page _____.

Details

Distinguish *between the* types of earthquakes *that occur at each type of plate boundary. Complete the table.*

	Divergent Boundary	**Convergent Boundary**	**Transform Boundary**
Type of stress			
Type of fault			
Magnitude of earthquake			

I found this information on page _____.

Organize *information about* earthquakes that occur away from plate boundaries. *Complete the concept map.*

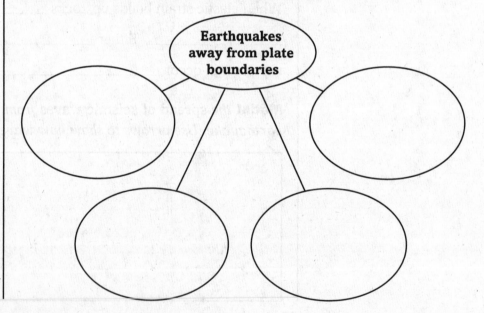

SUMMARIZE IT

Summarize the main ideas of the above section with two bullet points.

_____

_____

Name _Eden Tsunner_   Date _____

Earthquakes

Lesson 2 Earthquakes and Seismic Waves

 Grade 6 Science Content Standard—1.g: Students know how to determine the epicenter of an earthquake and know that the effects of an earthquake on any region vary, depending on the size of the earthquake, the distance of the region from the epicenter, the local geology, and the type of construction in the region. Also covers: 7.e

Predict *three topics that will be covered in Lesson 2. Use the headings and bold words to help.*

1. _____

2. _____

3. _____

Review Vocabulary

Use **wave** *in a scientific sentence. Use a dictionary or your book for help.*

wave   a disturbance in a mattarial that moves without transfir ing matter,

New Vocabulary

Write the correct term to match each definition in the blank.

___Swave___ compressional wave with particle motion in the same direction the wave travels

___Seismic Wave___ wave of energy produced at the focus of an earthquake

___Pwave___ shearing wave with particle motion perpendicular to the direction of wave travel

___epicenter___ point on Earth's surface directly above an earthquake focus

Academic Vocabulary

Use a dictionary to define the term **internal** *as it is used in the following sentence.*

Scientists study the internal structure of Earth.

internal   existing or situeated within the wm; or surface of something

Lesson 2 Earthquakes and Seismic Waves (continued)

Main Idea

Details

What are seismic waves?

I found this information on page _____.

Model *how energy travels during an earthquake as seismic waves. Draw a diagram showing how the energy travels. Label the* **epicenter** *and identify how the amount of energy changes with distance.*

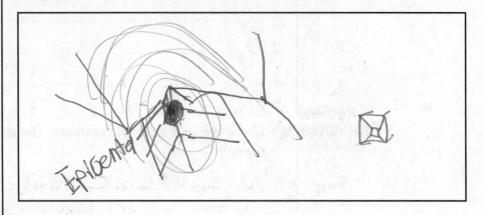

Epicenter

Classify *the three types of seismic waves. Describe each type of wave.*

Types of Seismic Waves

I found this information on page _____.

```
                    Seismic Waves
         ┌───────────────┼───────────────┐
    ┌─────────┐     ┌─────────┐     ┌─────────┐
    │         │     │         │     │         │
    └─────────┘     └─────────┘     └─────────┘
```

Description: particle motion in the same direction as the wave propagation; also called compressional waves	Description: also called	Description:

SUMMARIZE IT

Rephrase two main ideas from these sections in your own words.

_____

_____

_____

Lesson 2 Earthquakes and Seismic Waves (continued)

Main Idea

Details

Using Seismic Wave Data

I found this information on page _____.

Model *how* P-waves, S-waves, *and* surface waves *travel in an earthquake. Draw a diagram showing which waves arrive first.*

I found this information on page _____.

Outline *discoveries scientists have made using seismic waves.*

I. Internal structure

A. _____

_____

B. _____

_____

II. Shadow zone

A. Definition: _____

_____

B. _____

_____

SUMMARIZE IT

Summarize the main ideas of the above sections.

_____

_____

_____

_____

Earthquakes

Lesson 3 Measuring Earthquakes

 Grade 6 Science Content Standards—1.g: Students know how to determine the epicenter of an earthquake and know that the effects of an earthquake on any region vary, depending on the size of the earthquake, the distance of the region from the epicenter, the local geology, and the type of construction in the region. Also covers: 7.b, 7.g

Skim *Lesson 3, and predict three topics that you will study in this lesson.*

1. _____

2. _____

3. _____

Review Vocabulary **Define** sediment *using your book or a dictionary.*

sediment _____

_____

New Vocabulary *Use your book or a dictionary to define the following terms.*

seismograph _____

_____

_____

seismogram _____

_____

_____

Academic Vocabulary *Use the word* indicate *in a scientific sentence.*

indicate _____

_____

Lesson 3 **Measuring Earthquakes** (continued)

Main Idea

How are earthquakes measured?

I found this information on page _____.

Recording Seismic Waves

I found this information on page _____.

Locating an Epicenter

I found this information on page _____.

Details

Analyze *how scientists determined the size of the December 2004 Indian Ocean earthquake.*

_____

_____

Summarize *how a* mechanical seismograph *works.*

_____

_____

_____

Sequence *the steps scientists use to* locate the epicenter *of an earthquake. Complete the flow chart.*

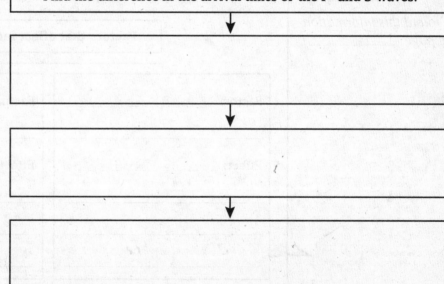

Find the difference in the arrival times of the P- and S-waves.

SUMMARIZE IT

Summarize one main idea from each section above.

_____

_____

_____

_____

Lesson 3 Measuring Earthquakes (continued)

Main Idea   ## Details

Measuring Earthquake Size

I found this information on page _____.

Distinguish *between the scales used to measure the* magnitude of earthquakes. *Describe the key features of each scale.*

Richter Magnitude Scale	Moment Magnitude
scale is based on magnitude values	scale is based on

Earthquake Intensity

I found this information on page _____.

Analyze *factors that affect* earthquake intensity. *Identify two factors that affect intensity, and summarize the effect of each.*

Factors that affect intensity

Factor: _____	Factor: _____
_____	_____
Effect: _____	Effect: _____
_____	_____
_____	_____

SUMMARIZE IT

Highlight the main ideas of each section above in the following passage.

Scientists use magnitude scales to measure the movement and energy released by earthquakes, and intensity to describe how much damage earthquakes cause. The Richter scale measures the amount of movement recorded on a seismogram. The moment magnitude is determined by the amount of energy released. It varies with the distance from the epicenter and the geology of the area.

Name _____   **Date** _____

Earthquakes
Lesson 4 Earthquake Hazards and Safety

 Grade 6 Science Content Standards—1.g: Students know how to determine the epicenter of an earthquake and know that the effects of an earthquake on any region vary, depending on the size of the earthquake, the distance of the region from the epicenter, the local geology, and the type of construction in the region. Also covers: 2.d, 7.a, 7.b

Scan *Lesson 4 of your book. Write three facts that you discovered about earthquake hazards and safety as you scanned the lesson.*

1. _____

   _____

2. _____

   _____

3. _____

   _____

Review Vocabulary **Define** San Andreas Fault *using your book or a dictionary.*

San Andreas Fault _____

_____

New Vocabulary *Use your book or a dictionary to define each of the following terms.*

liquefaction _____

_____

tsunami _____

_____

Academic Vocabulary *Use a dictionary to write the scientific definition for* securely. *Then use the word in a sentence.*

securely _____

_____

_____

Lesson 4 Earthquake Hazards and Safety (continued)

Main Idea

Details

Earthquake Hazards

I found this information on page _____.

Identify *five hazards that might result from an earthquake.*

Earthquakes can cause

_____ .
_____ .
_____ .
_____ .
_____ .

I found this information on page _____.

Explain *how* liquefaction *occurs and how it damages buildings.*

_____

_____

_____

I found this information on page _____.

Sequence *the events that cause a* tsunami. *Complete the flow chart.*

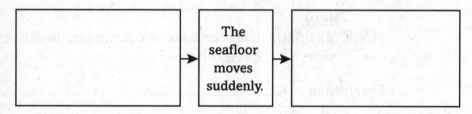

The seafloor moves suddenly.

Avoiding Earthquake Hazards

I found this information on page _____.

Summarize *how scientists determine the risk of earthquake hazards in an area.*

_____

_____

_____

SUMMARIZE IT

Summarize the main ideas of the above sections.

_____

_____

_____

Lesson 4 Earthquake Hazards and Safety (continued)

Main Idea ————————————— **Details**

Earthquakes and Structures

I found this information on page _____.

Outline *how* building planning *can help reduce loss of life during an earthquake.*

   I. Types of buildings

   A. _____

   _____

   B. _____

   _____

   II. Earthquake-resistant structures

   A. _____

   _____

   B. _____

   _____

Earthquake Safety

I found this information on page _____.

Model *tips for staying safe during and after an earthquake. Draw at least two safe behaviors for each environment.*

Indoors	Outdoors

SUMMARIZE IT Summarize two main ideas of the above sections of this lesson.

_____

_____

_____

Earthquakes Chapter Wrap-Up

Now that you have read the chapter, think about what you have learned and complete the table below. Compare your previous answers to these.

1. Write an **A** if you agree with the statement.

2. Write a **D** if you disagree with the statement.

Earthquakes	After You Read
• Plate movements cause earthquakes.	
• Scientists use earthquake waves to map the inside of Earth.	
• The Richter scale is the only way to measure the strength of an earthquake.	
• Fire is the most common hazard that occurs following an earthquake.	

Review

Use this checklist to help you study.

☐ Review the information you included in your Foldable.

☐ Study your *Science Notebook* on this chapter.

☐ Study the definitions of vocabulary words.

☐ Review daily homework assignments.

☐ Re-read the chapter and review the charts, graphs, and illustrations.

☐ Review the Standards Check at the end of each lesson.

☐ Look over the Standards Review at the end of the chapter.

SUMMARIZE IT

After reading this chapter, write a summary sentence for each lesson to illustrate the lesson's main ideas.

_____

_____

_____

_____

Volcanoes

Grade 6 Science Content Standards—1.e: Students know major geologic events, such as earthquakes, volcanic eruptions, and mountain building, result from plate motion. Also covers: 1.d–f, 2.d, 7.a, 7.b, 7.d, 7.g, 7.h

Before You Read

Before you read the chapter, respond to these statements.

1. Write an **A** if you agree with the statement.
2. Write a **D** if you disagree with the statement.

Before You Read	Volcanoes
	• A volcano forms when magma reaches Earth's surface.
	• Volcanic eruptions occur as a result of chemical reactions inside Earth.
	• All lava has the same composition.
	• Volcanic eruptions can change habitats for humans and wildlife.

Construct the Foldable as directed at the beginning of this chapter.

Science Journal

Make a list of what you might hear, smell, feel, see, and possibly taste while watching a volcanic eruption.

_____

_____

_____

_____

_____

_____

Volcanoes
Lesson 1 Volcanoes and Plate Boundaries

 Grade 6 Science Content Standards—1.e: Students know major geologic events, such as earthquakes, volcanic eruptions, and mountain building, result from plate motion. Also covers: 1.d, 7.b

Scan *Lesson 1 of your book. Use the checklist below.*

☐ Read all of the headings.

☐ Read all of the boldface words.

☐ Look at the charts, graphs, and pictures.

☐ Think about what you already know about volcanoes and plate boundaries.

Write three things that you will learn about volcanoes and plate boundaries.

1. _____

2. _____

3. _____

Review Vocabulary   **Define** lithospheric plate, *using your book or a dictionary.*

lithospheric plate _____

_____

New Vocabulary   *Write a paragraph that contains all of the vocabulary terms.*

volcano _____

hot spot _____

vent _____

fissure eruption _____

_____

_____

_____

_____

Academic Vocabulary   *Use a dictionary to define* source.

source _____

Lesson 1 Volcanoes and Plate Boundaries (continued)

Main Idea ———————————— Details

What is a volcano?

I found this information on page _____.

Distinguish magma *from* lava.

Magma: _____

Lava: _____

How do volcanoes form?

I found this information on page _____.

Sequence *the events that occur as a* volcano forms.

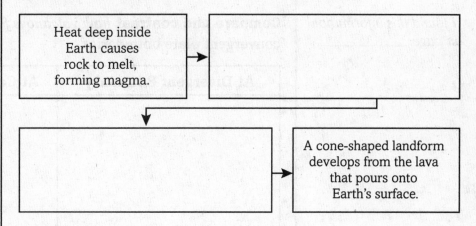

Heat deep inside Earth causes rock to melt, forming magma.	→	

| | | A cone-shaped landform develops from the lava that pours onto Earth's surface. |

I found this information on page _____.

Organize *information about* fissure eruptions *by completing the table.*

Fissure Eruptions	
When they occur	
Where they occur	
What they form	In oceans:
	On continents:

SUMMARIZE IT

Summarize the three main ideas of the above sections.

_____

_____

_____

_____

Lesson 1 Volcanoes and Plate Boundaries (continued)

⟨Main Idea⟩ _____ ⟨Details⟩ _____

Where do volcanoes occur?

I found this information on page _____.

Identify *the three places at which volcanoes often form.*

1. _____

2. _____

3. _____

I found this information on page _____.

Compare and contrast *how volcanoes form at* divergent *and* convergent plate boundaries.

At Divergent Boundary	At Convergent Boundary

I found this information on page _____.

Classify *the types of plates involved in the formation of each group of* landforms, *using the graphic organizer.*

Volcanic Landforms at Converging Plates

include

Island Arcs	

that form where   that form where

⟨**SUMMARIZE IT**⟩ Summarize the main idea of the above section.

_____

_____

Volcanoes

Lesson 2 Volcanic Eruptions and Features

 Grade 6 Science Content Standards—1.d: Students know that earthquakes are sudden motions along breaks in the crust called faults and that volcanoes and fissures are locations where magma reaches the surface. Also covers: 1.f, 7.g

Skim *Lesson 2 of your book. Write three questions that come to mind. Look for answers to your questions as you read the lesson.*

1. _____

2. _____

3. _____

Review Vocabulary *Use* landform *in a sentence to show its scientific meaning.*

landform

_____

_____

New Vocabulary *Use your book to define each vocabulary term.*

shield volcano

_____

_____

cinder cone volcano

_____

_____

tephra

_____

_____

composite volcano

_____

_____

Academic Vocabulary **Define** emerge, *using a dictionary.*

emerge

_____

_____

Lesson 2 Volcanic Eruptions and Features (continued)

Main Idea

Details

What controls volcanic eruptions?

I found this information on page _____.

Identify *three factors that affect how a volcano erupts.*

1. _____

2. _____

3 _____

I found this information on page _____.

Label *the arrow to show how the amount of silica in magma affects its viscosity.*

Low Viscosity   **High Viscosity**

_____ silica   _____ silica

Types of Magma and Lava

I found this information on page _____.

Compare and contrast basaltic magma and lava *and* granitic magma and lava.

	Basaltic	Granitic
Silica Content		
Viscosity		
Type of Eruption		

Contrast pahoehoe *lava and* aa *lava.*

Pahoehoe lava: _____

_____

Aa lava: _____

_____

SUMMARIZE IT

Summarize the main ideas of the above section.

_____

_____

_____

Lesson 2 Volcanic Eruptions and Features (continued)

Main Idea

Details

Types of Volcanoes

I found this information on page _____.

Organize *information about* the three types of volcanoes *by completing the graphic organizer.*

Volcano Types

Shield   Cinder Cone   Composite

Appearance:	Appearance:	Appearance:
Composition:	Composition:	Composition:
Formation:	Formation:	Formation:

I found this information on page _____.

Model *the three types of volcanoes by drawing a cross-section of each in the boxes provided.*

Shield Volcano	Cinder Cone Volcano	Composite Volcano

SUMMARIZE IT

Summarize the main idea of the above section.

_____

_____

Lesson 2 Volcanic Eruptions and Features (continued)

Main Idea

Volcanoes in California

I found this information on page _____.

Intrusive Volcanic Features and Other Volcanic Features

I found this information on page _____.

I found this information on page _____.

Details

Complete *the following paragraph.*

The _____ plate _____ beneath the

_____ plate. This forms a _____.

Part of this extends into _____.

Identify *features* of intrusive volcanoes. *Make a small sketch of each to help you remember what each one is.*

Intrusive Volcanic Features	

Model *the stages* of caldera formation *by drawing three pictures.*

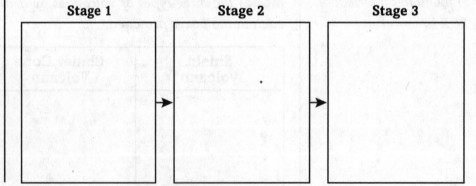

Stage 1   Stage 2   Stage 3

SUMMARIZE IT

Summarize two main ideas of the above sections.

_____

_____

_____

Volcanoes
Lesson 3 Hazards of Volcanic Eruptions

 Grade 6 Science Content Standards—2.d: Students know earthquakes, volcanic eruptions, landslides, and floods change human and wildlife habitat. Also covers: 7.a, 7.b, 7.d

Scan *Lesson 3 of your book. Read the headings, and look at the illustrations. Predict three things that will be discussed.*

1. _____

2. _____

3. _____

Review Vocabulary

Define seismic wave, *using your book or a dictionary.*

seismic wave _____

New Vocabulary

Use your book or a dictionary to define the vocabulary terms. Then use each term in a sentence that shows its scientific meaning.

volcanic ash _____
_____
_____
_____

lahar _____
_____
_____

pyroclastic flow _____
_____
_____
_____

Academic Vocabulary

Use a dictionary to define release. Then use the term in a sentence to show its scientific meaning.

release _____
_____

Lesson 3 Hazards of Volcanic Eruptions (continued)

Main Idea

Effects on Habitats

I found this information on page _____ .

Details

Organize *information by listing six hazards of volcanic eruptions.*

Hazards of volcanic eruptions include

I found this information on page _____ .

Identify *and describe information about the harm that* volcanic eruptions pose to habitats.

Volcanic Hazard	Potential Damage to Human or Natural Habitats
Volcanic Ash	
Landslides and Lahars	
Gases	
Pyroclastic Flows	
Lava Flows	

SUMMARIZE IT

Summarize the main idea of the above section.

_____

_____

_____

Lesson 3 Hazards of Volcanic Eruptions (continued)

Main Idea   **Details**

Predicting Volcanic Eruptions

I found this information on page _____.

Analyze *why each sign listed can be used to predict possible volcanic activity.*

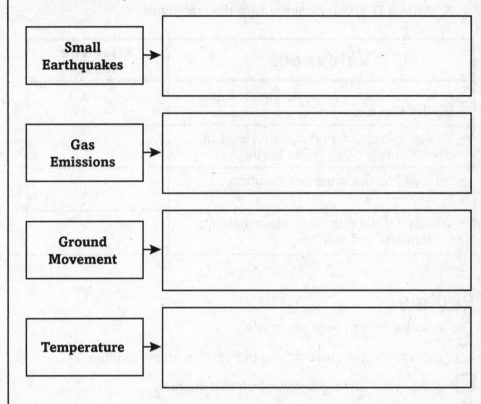

Small Earthquakes	→	
Gas Emissions	→	
Ground Movement	→	
Temperature	→	

Monitoring Volcanic Activity

I found this information on page _____.

Identify *three ways scientists monitor volcanic activity from space.*

Monitoring Volcanic Activity from Space

SUMMARIZE IT

Summarize two main ideas of the above sections in two bullet points.

_____

_____

_____

_____

Volcanoes Chapter Wrap-Up

Now that you have read the chapter, think about what you have learned and complete the table below. Compare your previous answers to these.

    1. Write an **A** if you agree with the statement.

    2. Write a **D** if you disagree with the statement.

Volcanoes	After You Read
• A volcano forms when magma reaches Earth's surface.	
• Volcanic eruptions occur as a result of chemical reactions inside Earth.	
• All lava has the same composition.	
• Volcanic eruptions can change habitats for humans and wildlife.	

Review

Use this checklist to help you study.

☐ Review the information you included in your Foldable.

☐ Study your *Science Notebook* on this chapter.

☐ Study the definitions of vocabulary words.

☐ Review daily homework assignments.

☐ Re-read the chapter and review the charts, graphs, and illustrations.

☐ Review the Standards Check at the end of each lesson.

☐ Look over the Standards Review at the end of the chapter.

SUMMARIZE IT   After studying the chapter, write one summary sentence for each lesson to illustrate the chapter's main ideas.

_____

_____

_____

_____

Name _____ Date _____

Weathering and Erosion

Grade 6 Science Content Standards—1.f: Students know how to explain major features of California geology (including mountains, faults, volcanoes) in terms of plate tectonics. Also covers: 2.a–d, 7.a–c, 7.e, 7.g

Before You Read

Before you read the chapter, respond to these statements.

1. Write an **A** if you agree with the statement.
2. Write a **D** if you disagree with the statement.

Before You Read	Weathering and Erosion
	• Soil is made of a mixture of weathered rocks, minerals, and organic matter.
	• Flowing water can move pieces of rock.
	• Most of California's coastal cliffs were formed by the action of waves.
	• Glaciers carve V-shaped valleys.

Construct the Foldable as directed at the beginning of this chapter.

Science Journal

Make a list of five things you know about the ocean. Select two of them and write a paragraph about each topic. Then, write a third paragraph that compares the two.

_____

_____

_____

_____

_____

_____

Weathering and Erosion
Lesson 1 Weathering

  Grade 6 Science Content Standards—2.a: Students know water running downhill is the dominant process in shaping the landscape, including California's landscape. Also covers: 7.e

Scan *the headings in Lesson 1 of your book. Identify four topics that will be discussed.*

1. _____

2. _____

3. _____

4. _____

Review Vocabulary

mineral

Define mineral *using your book or a dictionary.*

_____

_____

New Vocabulary

Read the definitions below. Write the correct vocabulary term on the blank to the left of each definition.

_____ mixture of weathered rock, minerals, and organic matter

_____ breakdown of rocks at Earth's surface from exposure to water and gases in the atmosphere

_____ destructive process that breaks down and changes rocks

_____ process that occurs when water freezes, expands, and melts in the cracks of rocks

_____ breaking of rock into smaller pieces without changing its mineral composition

Academic Vocabulary

contact

Define contact. *Use a dictionary to help you.*

_____

Name _____   Date _____

Lesson 1 Weathering (continued)

Main Idea   ## Details

What is weathering?

I found this information on page _____.

Organize *information by listing four* agents of weathering. *Give an example of each.*

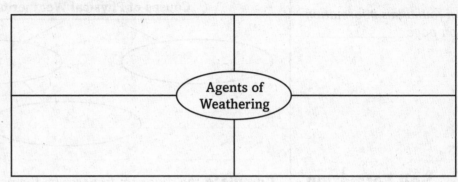

Agents of Weathering

I found this information on page _____.

Classify *the 2 types of* weathering processes.

Weathering processes

Chemical Weathering

I found this information on page _____.

Outline *information about* chemical weathering.

Chemical Weathering

I. Definition: _____

_____

II. Causes

    A. _____

    B. _____

    C. _____

    D. _____

SUMMARIZE IT

Summarize the main ideas of the above section.

_____

_____

_____

_____

Lesson 1 Weathering (continued)

Main Idea — Details

Physical Weathering

I found this information on page _____.

Identify *major causes of* physical weathering.

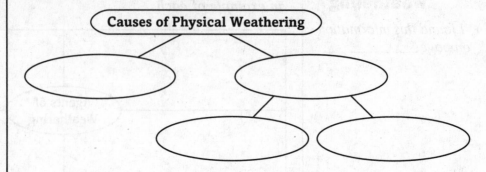

Soil Formation

I found this information on page _____.

Complete *the diagram to describe the process of* soil formation.

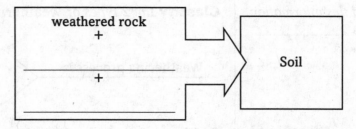

I found this information on page _____.

Label *the* soil profile *diagram to identify the composition of the* layers. Sketch the particles in each layer.

A Horizon (topsoil)	
B Horizon	
C Horizon	
Bedrock	

SUMMARIZE IT

Summarize three main ideas from the above section.

_____

_____

_____

Weathering and Erosion
Lesson 2 Erosion and Deposition

 Grade 6 Science Content Standards—2.a: Students know water running downhill is the dominant process in shaping the landscape, including California's landscape. Also covers: 2.b–d

Scan *the* What You'll Learn *statements for Lesson 2 of your book. Identify four topics that will be discussed.*

1. _____

2. _____

3. _____

4. _____

Review Vocabulary

Define sediment *using your book or a dictionary.*

sediment

_____

_____

New Vocabulary

Read the definitions below. Write the correct vocabulary term on the blank to the left of each definition.

_____ large mass of ice and snow

_____ event that occurs when the water level in a river rises above the usual height and overflows the sides of its banks

_____ landform consisting of loose sand and gravel

_____ form of erosion that is caused by gravity

_____ laying down of sediments in a new location

_____ rapid, gravity-caused event that moves soil, loose rocks, and boulders

_____ wide, flat valley located along the sides of some rivers and streams

Academic Vocabulary

Use a dictionary to define ultimate.

ultimate

_____

Lesson 2 Erosion and Deposition (continued)

Main Idea	Details

What are erosion and deposition?

I found this information on page _____.

Organize *information about* the causes of erosion by *completing the graphic organizer.*

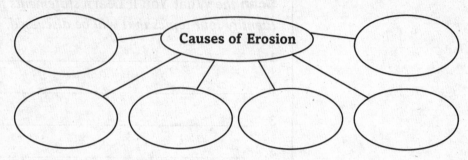

Mass Wasting

I found this information on page _____.

Classify *information about* types of mass wasting *by completing the concept map.*

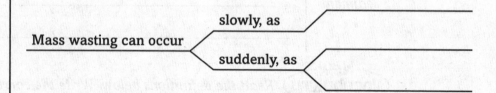

Water and Erosion

I found this information on page _____.

Model *three features that result when* streams deposit sediments *by sketching them below.*

Oxbow Lake	Alluvial Fan	Delta

SUMMARIZE IT

Summarize the three main ideas of the above section.

_____

_____

_____

_____

Lesson 2 Erosion and Deposition (continued)

Main Idea

Details

Shorelines and Erosion

I found this information on page _____ .

Contrast *five features formed by* wave erosion.

1. Cliff: _____

_____

2. Wave-cut platform: _____

_____

3. Marine terrace: _____

_____

4. Sea cave: _____

_____

5. Sea stack, sea arch: _____

_____

I found this information on page _____ .

Sequence *the 3 steps that create a* longshore current.

1. _____

2. _____

3. _____

I found this information on page _____ .

Model *how a* groin affects a shoreline. *Indicate where the groin would trap sediment.*

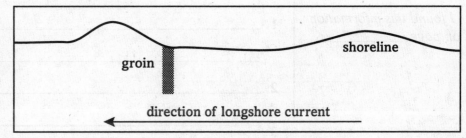

direction of longshore current

SUMMARIZE IT

Summarize the main ideas of the above section.

_____

_____

_____

Lesson 2 Erosion and Deposition (continued)

Main Idea

What are glaciers?

I found this information on page _____.

Details

Compare alpine glaciers *and* continental glaciers. *Use the phrases below to complete the Venn diagram.*

- form where more snow falls in summer than melts in winter
- cover entire land areas
- large masses of ice and snow
- also called ice sheets
- also called valley glaciers

- form high in mountains
- found only in Antarctica and Greenland
- flow from higher to lower elevations

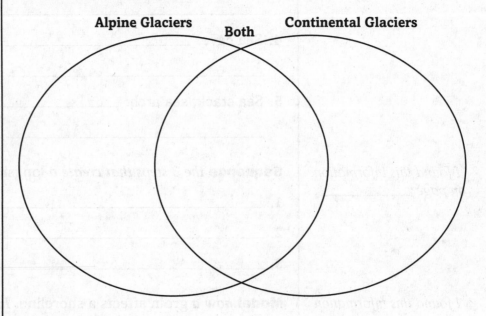

Alpine Glaciers   Both   Continental Glaciers

Wind

I found this information on page _____.

Identify *and describe two types of* **wind-blown deposits.**

1. _____

_____

2. _____

SUMMARIZE IT

Summarize two main ideas of the above sections of the lesson.

_____

_____

_____

Weathering and Erosion

Lesson 3 Reshaping the California Landscape

 Grade 6 Science Content Standards—1.f: Students know how to explain major features of California geology (including mountains, faults, volcanoes) in terms of plate tectonics. Also covers: 2.a, 2.b, 2.c, 7.d

Scan *Lesson 3 of your book. Read the headings and bold words and look at the pictures. Write three things that you learn about California landscapes.*

1. _____

_____

2. _____

_____

3. _____

_____

Review Vocabulary

uplift

Define uplift *using your book or a dictionary.*

_____

_____

New Vocabulary

basin and range

arroyo

Write a paragraph that includes all of the vocabulary terms.

_____

_____

_____

_____

_____

_____

_____

Academic Vocabulary

significant

Define significant *using a dictionary.*

_____

Lesson 3 Reshaping the California Landscape (continued)

| Main Idea | Details |

Mountain Landscapes

I found this information on page _____.

Identify *the 4 major types of landscapes in California.*

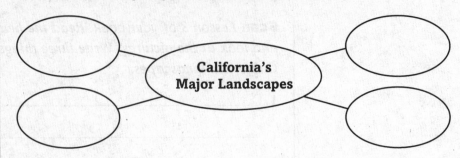

California's Major Landscapes

I found this information on page _____.

Distinquish erosional *and* depositional mountain features.

| Features of California's Mountains ||
Erosional Features	Depositional Features

Desert Landscapes

I found this information on page _____.

Compare *two types of desert landscapes by completing the Venn diagram with at least five facts.*

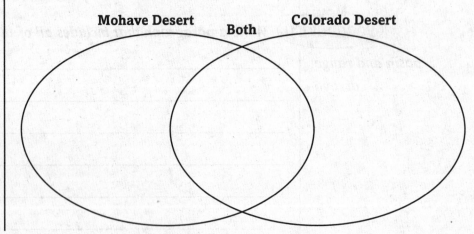

Mohave Desert | Both | Colorado Desert

SUMMARIZE IT

Summarize three main ideas of the above sections.

_____

_____

_____

Lesson 3 Reshaping the California Landscape (continued)

Main Idea	Details

The Central Valley

I found this information on page _____ .

Outline *information about the* Central Valley.

I. Description

    A. Location: _____

    B. Elevation: _____

II. Main Rivers

    A. _____

        _____

    B. _____

        _____

III. Other Features

    A. _____

        _____

    B. _____

        _____

Coastal Landscapes

I found this information on page _____ .

Model *three features that may result from* erosion *along* California's rocky coasts *by sketching them. Label the three features in your drawing.*

SUMMARIZE IT

Summarize the main ideas of the above section.

_____

_____

_____

Weathering and Erosion
Chapter Wrap-Up

Now that you have read the chapter, think about what you have learned and complete the table below. Compare your previous answers to these.

1. Write an **A** if you agree with the statement.

2. Write a **D** if you disagree with the statement.

Weathering and Erosion	After You Read
• Soil is made of a mixture of weathered rocks, minerals, and organic matter.	
• Flowing water can move pieces of rock.	
• Most of California's coastal cliffs were formed by the action of waves.	
• Glaciers carve V-shaped valleys.	

Review

Use this checklist to help you study.

☐ Review the information you included in your Foldable.

☐ Study your *Science Notebook* on this chapter.

☐ Study the definitions of vocabulary words.

☐ Review daily homework assignments.

☐ Re-read the chapter and review the charts, graphs, and illustrations.

☐ Review the Standards Check at the end of each lesson.

☐ Look over the Standards Review at the end of the chapter.

SUMMARIZE IT

After studying the chapter, write one summary sentence for each lesson to illustrate the chapter's main ideas.

_____

_____

_____

_____

Earth's Atmosphere

Grrade 6 Science Content Standards—4.a: Students know the sun is the major source of energy for phenomena on Earth's surface; it powers winds, ocean currents, and the water cycle. Also covers: 3.c, 3.d, 4.b, 4.d, 4.e, 7.c

Before You Read

Before you read the chapter, think about what you know about the topic. List three things that you already know about Earth's atmosphere in the first column. Then list three things that you would like to learn about Earth's atmosphere in the second column.

K What I know	W What I want to find out

Construct the Foldable as directed at the beginning of this chapter.

Science Journal

Write a hypothesis that explains how you think clouds form above Mount Shasta.

_____

_____

_____

_____

_____

_____

_____

Name _____   Date _____

Earth's Atmosphere
Lesson 1 Energy from the Sun

 Grade 6 Science Content Standards—4.a: Students know the sun is the major source of energy for phenomena on Earth's surface; it powers winds, ocean currents, and the water cycle. Also covers: 4.b

Skim *Lesson 1 of your book. Write three questions that come to mind. Look for answers to your questions as you read the lesson.*

1. _____

2. _____

3. _____

Review Vocabulary **Define** radiation.

radiation

_____

New Vocabulary *Read the definitions below. Write the correct vocabulary term on the blank to the left of each definition.*

_____ electromagnetic radiation with wavelengths shorter than visible light

_____ region of the atmosphere that extends from Earth's surface to a height of about 8km to 15 km

_____ entire range of wavelengths or frequencies of electromagnetic radiation

_____ region of the atmosphere that extends from about 15 km to 50 km

_____ electromagnetic radiation with longer wavelengths than visible light that is sometimes felt as heat

_____ mixture of gases that surround Earth

Academic Vocabulary *Use a dictionary to define* visible. *Then use it in a sentence to show its scientific meaning.*

visible

_____

_____

Lesson 1 Energy from the Sun (continued)

Main Idea	Details

Earth's Atmosphere

I found this information on page _____ .

Identify *the main* components *of the* atmosphere *and list their percentages.*

Composition of Earth's Atmosphere

_____ :

_____ %

_____ :

_____ %

_____ : 1%

Layers in the Atmosphere

I found this information on page _____ .

Label *the diagram to identify the locations of the four* layers of the atmosphere. *On the right side of the diagram, describe properties of each layer.*

Layers of the Atmosphere   **Properties of Layers**

1. _____ _____

2. _____ _____

3. _____ _____

4. _____ _____

Earth's Surface

SUMMARIZE IT

Summarize the main ideas of the above sections in two bullet points.

_____

_____

_____

Lesson 1 **Energy from the Sun** (continued)

Main Idea

Details

The Sun's Continuous Spectrum

I found this information on page _____.

Define electromagnetic spectrum. *Then list the 3 types of electromagnetic radiation that make up 99 percent of solar radiation.*

Electromagnetic spectrum: _____

_____

Solar radiation consists of:

1. _____

2. _____

3. _____

I found this information on page _____.

Compare and contrast infrared *and* ultraviolet radiation. *Complete the Venn diagram with at least five facts.*

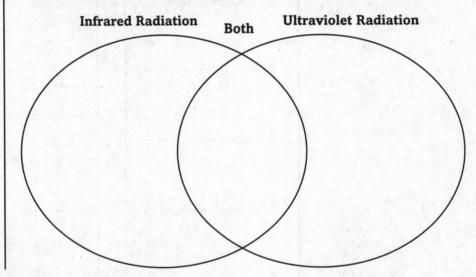

Infrared Radiation   Both   Ultraviolet Radiation

SUMMARIZE IT

Summarize three main ideas of the above section.

_____

_____

_____

_____

_____

Lesson 1 Energy from the Sun (continued)

Main Idea — Details

The Sun's Continuous Spectrum

I found this information on page _____.

Model *what happens to the Sun's radiation that strikes Earth's atmosphere. Make a drawing to show how much of the Sun's radiation reaches Earth's surface, is reflected back into space, and is absorbed by the atmosphere.*

The Sun's Power

I found this information on page _____.

Summarize *how the angle at which the Sun's radiation strikes Earth affects temperatures.*

_____

_____

_____

_____

I found this information on page _____.

Create *a concept map about the importance of* solar energy *on* Earth.

SUMMARIZE IT

Summarize two main ideas of the above sections.

_____

_____

_____

_____

Earth's Atmosphere
Lesson 2 Energy Transfer in the Atmosphere

Grade 6 Science Content Standards—4.d: Students know convection currents distribute heat in the atmosphere and oceans. Also covers: 3.c, 3.d

Scan the What You'll Learn *statements for Lesson 2 of your book.*
Identify three topics that will be discussed.

1. _____

2. _____

3. _____

Review Vocabulary **Define** convection, *using your book or a dictionary.*

convection _____

_____

New Vocabulary *Use your book or a dictionary to define the vocabulary terms.*
Use each term in a sentence that shows its scientific meaning.

inversion _____

_____

greenhouse gas _____

_____

global warming _____

_____

Academic Vocabulary *Use a dictionary to define* similar.

similar _____

Lesson 2 Energy Transfer in the Atmosphere (continued)

Main Idea ———————————————— **Details**

Conduction in Air

I found this information on page _____.

Complete *the graphic organizer below with the 3 types of* heat transfer.

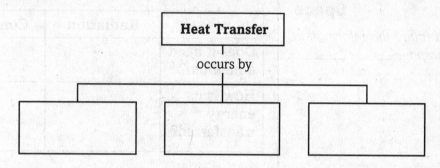

Convection in Air

I found this information on page _____.

Summarize *why increasing the temperature of air changes its density.*

_____

_____

_____

_____

I found this information on page _____.

Model *the way in which* convection currents *affect air circulation patterns in a room. Use arrows to show the path of air movement. Label the arrows to indicate warm air and cool air.*

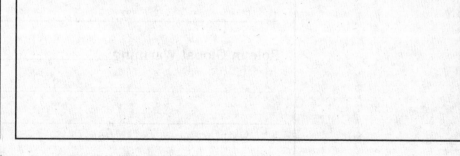

SUMMARIZE IT

Summarize the main ideas of the above sections in two bullet points.

_____

_____

_____

Lesson 2 Energy Transfer in the Atmosphere (continued)

Main Idea

Details

Radiation Traveling Through Space

I found this information on page _____.

Compare and contrast *the three forms of* heat transfer *in the chart.*

	Radiation	Conduction	Convection
Does it need a medium?			
How is its energy transferred?			

I found this information on page _____.

Create *a drawing to show how Earth maintains a* radiation balance.

I found this information on page _____.

Identify *three greenhouse gases. Then explain how scientists think greenhouse gases might play a role in global warming.*

1. _____   2. _____   3. _____

Role in Global Warming:_____

_____

_____

_____

SUMMARIZE IT

Summarize two main ideas of the above sections.

_____

_____

_____

Name _____   Date _____

Earth's Atmosphere
Lesson 3 Air Currents

 Grade 6 Science Content Standards—4.d: Students know convection currents distribute heat in the atmosphere and oceans. Also covers: 4.a, 4.e

Scan *Lesson 3 of your book. Use the checklist below.*

☐ Read all of the headings.

☐ Read all of the bold words.

☐ Look at the charts, graphs, and pictures.

☐ Think about what you already know about air currents.

Write three things that you have learned about air currents by scanning the lesson.

1. _____

2. _____

3. _____

Review Vocabulary

Define density *using your book or a dictionary.*

density _____

New Vocabulary

Write a paragraph that includes all of the vocabulary terms.

wind _____

updraft _____

downdraft _____

Coriolis effect _____

jet stream _____

_____

_____

_____

_____

_____

Academic Vocabulary

Define temporarily *using a dictionary.*

temporarily _____

Lesson 3 Air Currents (continued)

<table>
<tr><td>

⟨ Main Idea ⟩

</td><td>

⟨ Details ⟩

</td></tr>
<tr><td>

Local Winds and Eddies

I found this information on page _____.

</td><td>

Sequence *the Earth materials listed to indicate how rapidly each heats up when it absorbs solar radiation.*

- forest
- water
- sand
- snow and ice
- asphalt or concrete

Increasing temperature →

Less Radiation Absorbed			More Radiation Absorbed

1. _____   3. _____   4. _____

2. _____   5. _____

</td></tr>
<tr><td>

I found this information on page _____.

</td><td>

Create *two diagrams to show the movement of air in an* updraft *and a* downdraft. *Label each diagram to show heated, less dense air and cooler, denser air. Use arrows to show the direction of air movement.*

Updraft	**Downdraft**

</td></tr>
</table>

┌───┐
│ **SUMMARIZE IT** │
│ Summarize two main ideas of the above sections. │
│ _____ │
│ _____ │
│ _____ │
│ _____ │
└───┘

Lesson 3 Air Currents (continued)

Main Idea

Details

Air Currents Around Earth

I found this information on page _____.

Model *the directions in which winds blow in the Northern and Southern Hemispheres as a result of the* Coriolis effect. *Use arrows to draw the path followed by the winds.*

Northern Hemisphere Winds	Southern Hemisphere Winds

I found this information on page _____.

Complete *the graphic organizer below to identify the cells in the* three-cell model *of air movement.*

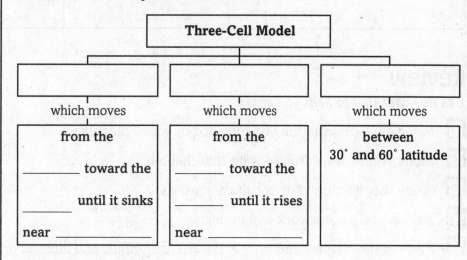

I found this information on page _____.

Define jet stream.

_____

_____

SUMMARIZE IT

Summarize three main ideas of the above sections.

_____

_____

_____

_____

Earth's Atmosphere Chapter Wrap-Up

Review the ideas you listed in the table at the beginning of the chapter. Cross out any incorrect information in the first column. Then complete the table by filling in the third column.

K What I know	W What I want to find out	L What I learned

Review

Use this checklist to help you study.

- ☐ Review the information you included in your Foldable.
- ☐ Study your *Science Notebook* on this chapter.
- ☐ Study the definitions of vocabulary words.
- ☐ Review daily homework assignments.
- ☐ Re-read the chapter and review the charts, graphs, and illustrations.
- ☐ Review the Standards Check at the end of each lesson.
- ☐ Look over the Standards Review at the end of the chapter.

SUMMARIZE IT
After studying the chapter, write one summary sentence for each lesson to illustrate the chapter's main ideas.

_____

_____

_____

_____

Oceans

Grade 6 Science Content Standards—7.f: Students will read a topographic map and a geologic map for evidence provided on the maps and construct and interpret a simple scale map. Also covers: 1.e, 2.c, 4.a, 4.d, 7.c

Before You Read

Before you read the chapter, think about what you know about the topic. List three things that you already know about oceans in the first column. Then list three things that you would like to learn about oceans in the second column.

K What I know	W What I want to find out

Construct the Foldable as directed at the beginning of this chapter.

Science Journal

Near Earth's poles, where the angle of sunlight is low, the water is cold. Write a hypothesis that explains how warm ocean currents reach higher latitudes and cold ocean currents reach lower latitudes.

_____

_____

_____

_____

_____

_____

Oceans
Lesson 1 Earth's Oceans

Grade 6 Science Content Standards—7.f: Students will read a topographic map and a geologic map for evidence provided on the maps and construct and interpret a simple scale map. Also covers: 7.c

Scan *Lesson 1 of your book. Write three facts you discovered about Earth's oceans while scanning the lesson.*

1. _____

2. _____

3. _____

Review Vocabulary

Define topographic map. *Then use the term in a sentence.*

topographic map   _____

_____

New Vocabulary

Use your book or a dictionary to define the following terms.

sea level   _____

_____

ocean floor   _____

_____

bathymetric map   _____

_____

echo sounding   _____

_____

continental shelf   _____

_____

Academic Vocabulary

Use the word method *in a scientific sentence.*

method   _____

Lesson 1 Earth's Oceans (continued)

Main Idea

Details

Mapping Earth's Oceans

I found this information on page _____ .

Organize *information about* Earth's 5 major oceans *by completing the table.*

Name	Characteristics
Pacific Ocean	

I found this information on page _____ .

Complete *the paragraph to describe* how sound is used to measure depth.

An instrument attached to _____ emits a sound wave. Depth is determined by the time it takes the sound to _____

_____ . The _____ it takes, the

_____ the depth.

SUMMARIZE IT

Summarize the main ideas of the above sections with two bullet points.

_____

_____

_____

Lesson 1 Earth's Oceans (continued)

Main Idea

Details

The Ocean Floor

I found this information on page _____.

Define *and describe the 5 typical geologic features of the ocean floor.*

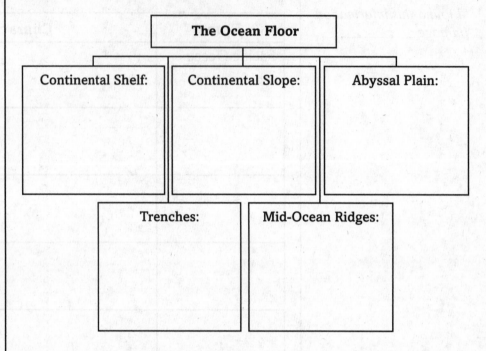

Model *the features of the ocean floor. Draw and label a* bathymetric profile *showing each of the features that you defined above in the graphic organizer.*

I found this information on page _____.

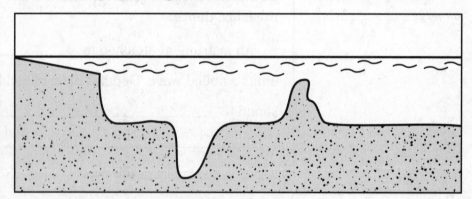

SUMMARIZE IT

Summarize two main ideas of the above section.

_____
_____
_____

Name _____ **Date** _____

Oceans

Lesson 2 Ocean Currents

 Grade 6 Science Content Standards—4.d: Students know convection currents distribute heat in the atmosphere and oceans. Also covers: 4.a

Scan *the headings in Lesson 2 of this chapter. Predict three topics that will be discussed.*

1. _____

2. _____

3. _____

Review Vocabulary

latitude

Define latitude *using your book or a dictionary.*

_____

_____

New Vocabulary

Read the definitions below. Write the correct vocabulary term on the blank to the left of each definition. Then write a paragraph containing the vocabulary terms.

_____   river in the ocean

_____   amount of salt dissolved in water

_____   cycle of currents

_____

_____

_____

_____

_____

Academic Vocabulary

cycle

Use your book or a dictionary to define the term cycle. *Then use the term in a sentence to show its scientific meaning.*

_____

_____

Lesson 2 Ocean Currents (continued)

Main Idea

Influences on Ocean Currents

I found this information on page _____.

I found this information on page _____.

I found this information on page _____.

Details

Identify *six things that are moved from place to place by* ocean currents.

1. _____   4. _____

2. _____   5. _____

3. _____   6. _____

Summarize how the oceans help equalize the amount of heat throughout the planet.

_____

_____

Model *how the* Coriolis effect deflects ocean currents *in the northern and southern hemispheres. Use arrows to indicate the direction of currents.*

SUMMARIZE IT

Summarize two main ideas of the above sections.

_____

_____

_____

_____

Name _____ Date _____

Lesson 2 Ocean Currents (continued)

Main Idea

Influences on Ocean Currents

I found this information on page _____.

I found this information on page _____.

I found this information on page _____.

Details

Complete *the flow chart to describe the process that forms* **deep ocean currents** *in Antarctica.*

| Surface water is _____ by air. | → | Salinity _____ as some water freezes. | → | Surface water becomes _____ and _____. |

Model *the currents that make up the* **North Pacific Gyre** *using labeled arrows.*

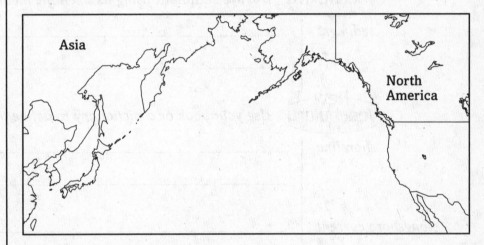

Asia

North America

Analyze *the causes and effects of* El Niño *and* La Niña.

Event	Cause	Effect
El Niño		
La Niña		

SUMMARIZE IT

Summarize the main ideas of the above sections in your own words.

_____

_____

_____

Name _____ Date _____

Oceans

Lesson 3 The Ocean Shore

 Grade 6 Science Content Standards—2.c: Students know beaches are dynamic systems in which the sand is supplied by rivers and moved along the coast by the action of waves.

Skim *Lesson 3 and predict three topics that you will study.*

1. _____

2. _____

3. _____

Review Vocabulary

Define sediment *using its scientific meaning.*

sediment

_____

_____

New Vocabulary

Use your book or a dictionary to define the following terms.

shoreline

_____

_____

longshore current

_____

_____

longshore drift

_____

_____

rip current

_____

_____

Academic Vocabulary

Use a dictionary to find the scientific definition of the term suspend.

suspend

_____

Lesson 3 The Ocean Shore (continued)

◄ Main Idea ►   ◄ Details ►

Shoreline Processes

I found this information on page _____.

Summarize forces that erode the shoreline.

Erosion by Wind and Waves	
Forces	Effects
Wind	
Waves	
Water	

I found this information on page _____.

Distinguish *two factors that affect the* rate of shoreline erosion.

1. _____

2. _____

I found this information on page _____.

Draw longshore current *and* longshore drift. *Use arrows to show the direction of waves and movement of sediment.*

┌─────────────────────────────────┐
│   │
│   │
│   │
│   │
│   │
│   │
└─────────────────────────────────┘

SUMMARIZE IT

Summarize the main ideas of the above sections.

_____

_____

Lesson 3 The Ocean Shore (continued)

Main Idea   ## Details

Shoreline Processes

I found this information on page _____.

Analyze *how* rip currents *form.*

_____

_____

_____

I found this information on page _____.

Summarize *two unintended results caused by structures built by humans.*

Jetties, groins, and breakwaters: _____

_____

Seawalls: _____

_____

Sand and Weathered Material

I found this information on page _____.

Organize *the following sediment sizes from largest to smallest:* sand, boulder, gravel, silt, clay, *and* cobble.

_____

Sequence *the steps that* form sand.

Weathering _____		Rivers _____
_____	→	_____ and
_____.		_____.

Currents _____.

SUMMARIZE IT

Highlight one main idea of this section in the paragraph below.

Weathering breaks large boulders into smaller rocks. Rain then washes small rocks into rivers. Rivers transport these rocks to the ocean. Along the way, rocks are continually weathered and broken down into smaller and smaller pieces. These small pieces are then transported along the shoreline.

Oceans

Lesson 4 Living on the California Coast

 Grade 6 Science Content Standards—4.d: Students know convection currents distribute heat in the atmosphere and oceans. Also covers: 1.e, 7.c, 7.f

Scan *Lesson 4 of your book using the checklist below.*

☐ Read all the lesson titles.

☐ Read all the boldface words.

☐ Look at all the pictures.

☐ Think about what you already know about the California coast.

Ask three questions about the topic.

1. _____

2. _____

3. _____

Review Vocabulary

Define transform plate boundary *using your book or a dictionary.*

transform plate boundary

_____

_____

New Vocabulary

Write the vocabulary terms to the left of their definitions.

_____ narrow, warm water current that flows north from the tropics

_____ large, slow-moving current that travels in a southward direction bringing cool water from northern latitudes

_____ related to the ocean

_____ place in which an organism lives

Academic Vocabulary

Use a dictionary to define region. *Then use it in a sentence to show its scientific meaning.*

region

_____

_____

Lesson 4 Living on the California Coast (continued)

Main Idea _____ **Details** _____

Geology of the California Coast

I found this information on page _____.

Summarize *the tectonic activity that has affected the California coast in the past and present by completing the paragraph.*

Most of California lies on _____, and the

Pacific Ocean rests on _____. Until about

30 million years ago, _____. Then the direction

of their movement changed and they started _____

_____. This lifted and crushed _____.

I found this information on page _____.

Analyze *why California has so many rocky beaches.*

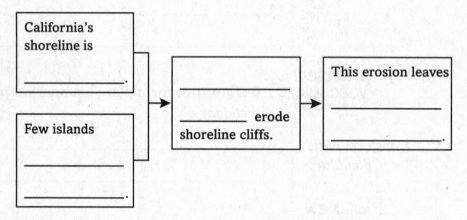

California's shoreline is _____.

Few islands _____. _____.

_____ erode shoreline cliffs.

This erosion leaves _____.

I found this information on page _____.

Complete *the graphic organizer to identify the* causes of tsunamis. *Underline the cause that results in the largest tsunamis.*

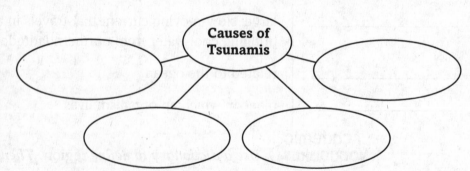

Causes of Tsunamis

┌─ SUMMARIZE IT ───┐
│ Summarize the main ideas of the above sections.   │
│   │
│ _____   │
│   │
│ _____   │
└──┘

Lesson 4 Living on the California Coast (continued)

⟨Main Idea⟩ ——————— ⟨Details⟩

Currents Along the Coast

I found this information on page _____.

Model *and label the two major currents along the California coast.*

Summarize *why there are* no hurricanes in California.

I found this information on page _____.

When a storm system curves northward and eastward toward

California, it reaches the _____ of the California

current and _____.

Identify *two factors which account for the* abundant marine life *found at the Channel Islands.*

I found this information on page _____.

1. _____

2. _____

Create *and label a sketch of the* intertidal zone.

I found this information on page _____.

SUMMARIZE IT

Summarize the above section of this lesson.

_____

_____

_____

Oceans Chapter Wrap-Up

Review the ideas you listed in the table at the beginning of the chapter. Cross out any incorrect information in the first column. Then complete the table by filling in the third column.

K What I know	W What I want to find out	L What I learned

Review

Use this checklist to help you study.

☐ Review the information you included in your Foldable.

☐ Study your *Science Notebook* on this chapter.

☐ Study the definitions of vocabulary words.

☐ Review daily homework assignments.

☐ Re-read the chapter and review the charts, graphs, and illustrations.

☐ Review the Standards Check at the end of each lesson.

☐ Look over the Standards Review at the end of the chapter.

SUMMARIZE IT After reading this chapter, write one summary sentence for each lesson to illustrate the chapter's main ideas.

_____

_____

_____

_____

Weather and Climate

Grade 6 Science Content Standards—4.a: Students know the sun is the major source of energy for phenomena on Earth's surface; it powers winds, ocean currents, and the water cycle. Also covers: 2.d, 4.d, 4.e

Before You Read

Before you read the chapter, think about what you already know about the topic. List three things that you already know about weather and climate in the first column. Then list three things that you would like to learn about weather and climate in the second column.

K What I know	W What I want to find out

FOLDABLES
Study Organizer

Construct the Foldable as directed at the beginning of this chapter.

Science Journal

Describe your observations of California's weather, climate, and seasons. Analyze the importance of water in your descriptions.

_____

_____

_____

_____

_____

_____

_____

Name _____ Date _____

Weather and Climate
Lesson 1 Weather

 Grade 6 Science Content Standards—4.a: Students know the sun is the major source of energy for phenomena on Earth's surface; it powers winds, ocean currents, and the water cycle. Also covers: 4.e

Scan *the headings of the paragraphs throughout Lesson 1. Identify two topics that you will learn about.*

1. _____

2. _____

Review Vocabulary *Use your book or a dictionary to define* wind.

wind | _____

New Vocabulary *Write the vocabulary term to the left of its definition.*

_____ | cycle in which water constantly moves between the hydrosphere and the atmosphere

_____ | temperature at which air becomes fully saturated with water vapor and condensation forms

_____ | atmospheric conditions, along with short term changes, of a certain place at a certain time

_____ | amount of water vapor present in air

_____ | amount of water vapor in the air relative to the maximum amount of water vapor the air can hold at that temperature before becoming saturated

_____ | water, in liquid or solid form, that falls from the atmosphere

Academic Vocabulary *Use a dictionary to define* traditionally.

traditionally | _____

_____

Lesson 1 Weather (continued)

Main Idea

Weather Factors

I found this information on page _____.

Details

Organize *information by listing and briefly describing* factors that describe weather.

Factors That Describe Weather	
Factor	Description
air temperature	
	pressure that a column of air exerts on the air below it

I found this information on page _____.

Identify *four types of* precipitation *and describe their forms when they reach Earth's surface.*

Types of Precipitation			
rain: water droplets			

SUMMARIZE IT

Summarize a main idea of this section.

_____

_____

_____

Lesson 1 Weather (continued)

Main Idea

The Water Cycle

I found this information on page _____ .

I found this information on page _____ .

Details

Label *the graph about water in the* **hydrosphere.**

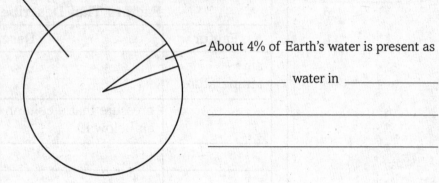

About 96% of Earth's water is stored in _____ .

About 4% of Earth's water is present as

_____ water in _____

_____

_____

Model *the water cycle in the space below.*

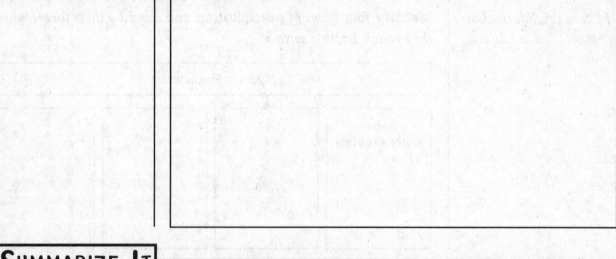

SUMMARIZE IT
bullet points.

Summarize three main ideas of the above sections with three

_____

_____

_____

Weather and Climate
Lesson 2 Weather Patterns

 Grade 6 Science Content Standards—4.e: Students know differences in pressure, heat, air movement, and humidity result in changes in weather. Also covers: 2.d

Scan *the headings throughout Lesson 2. Write three questions about topics covered in the lesson.*

1. _____

2. _____

3. _____

Review Vocabulary

Define atmosphere, *using your book or dictionary.*

atmosphere

_____

New Vocabulary

Read the definitions below. Write the correct vocabulary term on the blank to the left of each definition.

_____ regular change in temperature and length of day that result from the tilt of Earth's axis

_____ flood that takes place suddenly

_____ colder air moving toward warmer air and pushing it upwards

_____ body of air that has consistent weather features

_____ lighter, warmer air moving over heavier, colder air

_____ period of time when precipitation is much lower than normal or absent

Academic Vocabulary

Find the sentence in this lesson that uses the word consequence, *and write the sentence below.*

consequence _____

_____

_____

Lesson 2 Weather Patterns (continued)

Main Idea

The Changing Weather

I found this information on page _____.

I found this information on page _____.

I found this information on page _____.

Details

Summarize *information about the characteristics of an air mass's key weather features.*

The weather features that characterize an air mass include

_____ and _____. An air mass gets

its characteristics from _____.

Create *a diagram of a warm front and a cold front in the space below. Include labels for the air masses in your diagram.*

Warm Front	Cold Front

Predict *what will happen to the air pressure near Earth's surface as air moves vertically.*

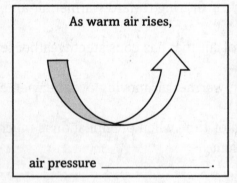

As warm air rises,

air pressure _____.

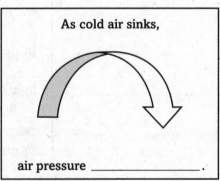

As cold air sinks,

air pressure _____.

SUMMARIZE IT

paragraph.

Summarize the main ideas of the above sections in a short

_____

_____

_____

Lesson 2 Weather Patterns (continued)

Main Idea	Details

Cycles that Affect Weather

I found this information on page _____.

Identify *and briefly describe three cycles that affect the weather.*

Cycles that Affect the Weather

day and night: daily cycle of warming and cooling of air and ground

Severe Weather

I found this information on page _____.

Organize *information about droughts and floods in the table.*

	Droughts	**Floods**
Caused by:		extended periods of
May result in:	major decrease in	
Recent occurrences:		

Summarize *why the damage from flash floods is increasing.*

_____

_____

SUMMARIZE IT

Summarize a main idea of the above sections.

_____

_____

Weather and Climate
Lesson 3 Climate

 Grade 6 Science Content Standards—4.d: Students know convection currents distribute heat in the atmosphere and oceans. Also covers: 4.e

Scan *the headings and illustrations in Lesson 3 of your book. Write two questions about this lesson that come to mind.*

1. _____

2. _____

Review Vocabulary

Define habitat *using your book or a dictionary.*

habitat _____

New Vocabulary

Use your book to define the following terms. Then write a sentence that uses them.

climate _____

_____

mediterranean climate _____

_____

highland climate _____

_____

Sentence: _____

_____

_____

Academic Vocabulary

Use a dictionary to define **affect.** *Then use it in a sentence to show its meaning.*

affect _____

_____

Lesson 3 Climate (continued)

◄Main Idea►

◄Details►

A World of Many Climates

I found this information on page _____ .

Compare *the* mediterranean climate *and the* highland climate.

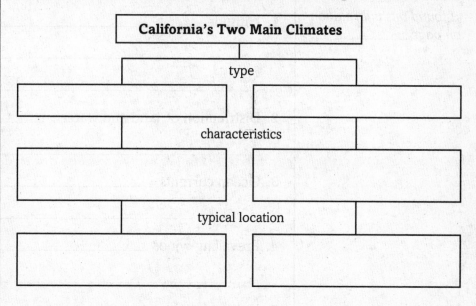

California's Two Main Climates

type

characteristics

typical location

I found this information on page _____ .

Distinguish *between California's main regions of* mediterranean climate *from its main regions of* highland climate *by marking and labeling the map.*

SUMMARIZE IT

Summarize two of the main ideas of the above sections.

_____

_____

_____

Lesson 3 Climate (continued)

Main Idea

Details

Climate Controls

I found this information on page _____.

Summarize *how* climate controls *affect climate.*

1. Latitude _____

_____

_____

2. Distribution of land and water _____

_____

3. Ocean currents _____

_____

4. Prevailing winds _____

_____

5. Human influences on climate _____

I found this information on page _____.

Sequence *the changes that some scientists think could result from* **global warming.**

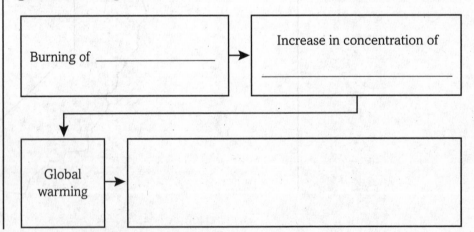

SUMMARIZE IT

Summarize the main idea of the above section in a single sentence.

_____

_____

Name _____   Date _____

Weather and Climate
Lesson 4 California Climate and Local Weather Patterns

 Grade 6 Science Content Standards—4.d: Students know convection currents distribute heat in the atmosphere and oceans. Also covers: 4.e

Scan *the headings and illustrations in Lesson 4 of your book. Write three topics that you think will be discussed in this lesson.*

1. _____

2. _____

3. _____

Review Vocabulary

Define California Current, *using your book or dictionary.*

California Current   _____

_____

New Vocabulary

Use your book to define the following terms.

rain shadow   _____

sea breeze   _____

land breeze   _____

valley breeze   _____

mountain breeze   _____

Santa Ana wind   _____

Academic Vocabulary

Use a dictionary to define accumulate. *Then use it in a sentence to show its meaning.*

accumulate   _____

_____

_____

Lesson 4 California Climate and Local Weather Patterns

Main Idea   **Details**

Mediterranean and Highland Climates

I found this information on page _____.

Identify three factors that affect the climates of California.

California's climates
are influenced by ⟨ _____
                    _____
                    _____

I found this information on page _____.

Sequence *the formation of fog along the California coast.*

Westerlies _____ _____ .

↓

The warm air crosses over the _____ of the California current.

↓

I found this information on page _____.

Model *and label the formation of a rain shadow.*

SUMMARIZE IT Summarize three main ideas of the above sections with two bullet points.

_____

_____

Lesson 4 California Climate and Local Weather Patterns

Main Idea _____ Details

Local Winds

I found this information on page _____.

Model *the formation of a sea breeze in a sketch.*

I found this information on page _____.

Compare and contrast valley breezes *and* mountain breezes *in the Venn diagram with at least five facts.*

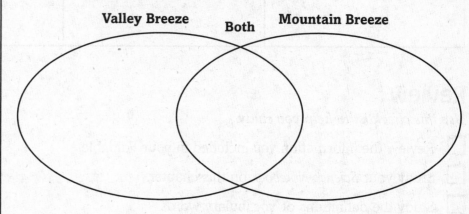

Valley Breeze   Both   Mountain Breeze

I found this information on page _____.

Rephrase *how Santa Ana winds can lead to fires in southern California.*

_____

_____

_____

SUMMARIZE IT

Summarize the three main ideas of the above sections with three bullet points.

_____

_____

_____

_____

Weather and Climate Chapter Wrap-Up

Review the ideas you listed in the table at the beginning of the chapter. Cross out any incorrect information in the first column. Then complete the table by filling out the third column.

K What I know	W What I want to find out	L What I learned

Review

Use this checklist to help you study.

☐ Review the information you included in your Foldable.

☐ Study your *Science Notebook* on this chapter.

☐ Study the definitions of vocabulary words.

☐ Review daily homework assignments.

☐ Re-read the chapter and review the charts, graphs, and illustrations.

☐ Review the Standards Check at the end of each lesson.

☐ Look over the Standards Review at the end of the chapter.

SUMMARIZE IT
After studying the chapter, write one summary sentence for each section to illustrate that chapter's main ideas.

_____

_____

_____

_____

Ecological Roles

Grade 6 Science Content Standards—5.e: Students know the number and types of organisms an ecosystem can support depends on the resources available and on abiotic factors, such as quantities of light and water, a range of temperatures, and soil composition. Also covers: 4.a, 5.c, 5.d, 7.a, 7.b, 7.c, 7.d

Before You Read

Before you read the chapter, respond to these statements.

1. Write an **A** if you agree with the statement.
2. Write a **D** if you disagree with the statement.

Before You Read	Ecological Roles
	• An ecosystem consists only of the living things in an area.
	• Soil, sunlight, water, and temperature help determine which organisms can live in an area.
	• Animals and plants that live in the desert do not need water.
	• A niche is an organism's role in its community.

Construct the Foldable as directed at the beginning of this chapter.

Science Journal

Write three questions you have about the photo that you might like to explore further.

_____

_____

_____

_____

_____

_____

Ecological Roles
Lesson 1 Biotic and Abiotic Factors

Grade 6 Science Content Standards—5.e: Students know the number and types of organisms an ecosystem can support depends on the resources available and on abiotic factors, such as quantities of light and water, a range of temperatures, and soil composition. Also covers: 4.a, 7.c

Skim *the headings in Lesson 1 of your book. Identify three topics that will be discussed.*

1. _____

2. _____

3. _____

Review Vocabulary **Define** climate *using your book or a dictionary.*

climate

_____

_____

New Vocabulary *Read the definitions below. Write the correct vocabulary term on the blank to the left of each definition.*

_____ living part of an ecosystem

_____ dark-colored soil material that makes nutrients available to plants

_____ group of organisms that share similar characteristics and can reproduce among themselves producing fertile offspring

_____ all the species that occupy an area

_____ nonliving part of an ecosystem

_____ number of individuals of one species that occupy an area

_____ an environmental factor that limits the population of organisms in an ecosystem

_____ the organisms in an area and the place they live

Academic Vocabulary *Use your book or a dictionary to define* adapt *to show its scientific meaning.*

adapt

_____

Lesson 1 Biotic and Abiotic Factors (continued)

Main Idea | **Details**

What is an ecosystem?

I found this information on page _____.

Define ecosystem, *and describe some interactions that take place in an ecosystem. Give two examples.*

_____

_____

_____

Examples: _____

_____

_____

Abiotic Factors

I found this information on page _____.

Organize *information about the abiotic factors that are found in an ecosystem. Give one example of how each affects organisms.*

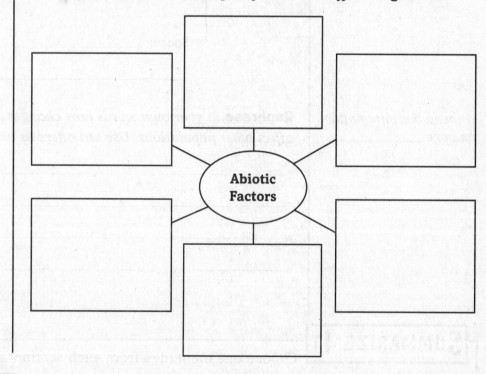

SUMMARIZE IT Summarize three main ideas of the above sections.

_____

_____

_____

Lesson 1 Biotic and Abiotic Factors (continued)

Main Idea

Biotic Factors and **Limiting Factors**

I found this information on page _____.

Details

Organize *information about* limiting factors. *Describe how each limiting factor affects populations in an ecosystem.*

Limiting Factors

Food: _____

_____

Water: _____

_____

Shelter: _____

_____

Space: _____

_____

I found this information on page _____.

Rephrase *in your own words how changes in one population can affect other populations. Use sea otters as an example.*

_____

_____

_____

_____

SUMMARIZE IT

Choose one main idea from each section above. Summarize the main idea in your own words.

_____

_____

_____

_____

Ecological Roles
Lesson 2 Organisms and Ecosystems

 Grade 6 Science Content Standards—5.d: Students know populations of organisms can be categorized by the functions they serve in an ecosystem. Also covers: 5.c, 5.e, 7.a

Scan *Lesson 2 of your book. Write three facts that you discover about organisms and ecosystems.*

1. _____

_____

2. _____

_____

3. _____

_____

Review Vocabulary **Define** latitude.

latitude

_____

_____

New Vocabulary *Write a paragraph using all the vocabulary terms.*

biome _____

niche _____

habitat _____

_____

_____

_____

Academic Vocabulary *Use a dictionary to define* migrate. *Then use the term in a sentence to show its scientific meaning.*

migrate _____

_____

Lesson 2 Organisms and Ecosystems (continued)

Main Idea

Biomes

I found this information on page _____.

Details

Outline *information about four biomes found in the world.*

   I. Tundra

   A. _____

   B. _____

   II. Taiga

   A. _____

   B. _____

   III. Rain Forest

   A. Types and locations

   1. _____

   2. _____

   B. Shared characteristics

   1. _____

   2. _____

   IV. Grassland

   A. _____

   B. _____

I found this information on page _____.

Identify *and describe climate features of California biomes.*

Temperate Deciduous Forest	Desert	Chapparal

SUMMARIZE IT

Summarize two main ideas of the above section of this lesson.

_____

_____

Lesson 2 Organisms and Ecosystems (continued)

| Main Idea | Details |

Habitat and Niches

I found this information on page _____.

Organize *information about an organism's* niche. *Complete the concept map.*

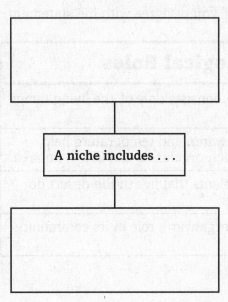

A niche includes . . .

Human Impacts on Niches

I found this information on page _____.

Analyze *how* human action can affect an ecosystem. *Sequence causes and effects.*

Humans do not allow fire to burn in chaparral.

| | SUMMARIZE IT |

Summarize two main ideas of the above sections.

_____

_____

_____

_____

Ecological Roles Chapter Wrap-Up

Now that you have read the chapter, think about what you have learned and complete the table below. Compare your previous answers to these.

1. Write an **A** if you agree with the statement.
2. Write a **D** if you disagree with the statement.

Ecological Roles	After You Read
• An ecosystem consists only of the living things in an area.	
• Soil, sunlight, water, and temperature help determine which organisms can live in an area.	
• Animals and plants that live in the desert do not need water.	
• A niche is an organism's role in its community.	

Review

Use this checklist to help you study.

☐ Review the information you included in your Foldable.

☐ Study your *Science Notebook* on this chapter.

☐ Study the definitions of vocabulary words.

☐ Review daily homework assignments.

☐ Re-read the chapter and review the charts, graphs, and illustrations.

☐ Review the Standards Check at the end of each lesson.

☐ Look over the Standards Review at the end of the chapter.

SUMMARIZE IT After reading the chapter, write a summary sentence for each lesson to illustrate the chapter's main ideas.

_____

_____

_____

_____

Name _____ Date _____

Energy and Matter in Ecosystems

 Grade 6 Science Content Standards—5.a: Students know energy entering ecosystems as sunlight is transferred by producers into chemical energy through photosynthesis and then from organism to organism through food webs. Also covers: 5.b, 5.c, 7.b, 7.d, 7.e, 7.g

Before You Read

Before you read the chapter, respond to these statements.

  1. Write an **A** if you agree with the statement.

  2. Write a **D** if you disagree with the statement.

Before You Read	Energy and Matter in Ecosystems
	• An ecosystem is made up of both living and nonliving things.
	• Plants make their own food.
	• Energy cycles through ecosystems.
	• All living things release some food energy as heat.

 *Construct the Foldable as directed at the beginning of this chapter.*

Science Journal

Write a paragraph on what you know about energy and matter in ecosystems.

_____
_____
_____
_____
_____
_____

Name _____   Date _____

Energy and Matter in Ecosystems
Lesson 1 Producers and Consumers

 Grade 6 Science Content Standards—5.a: Students know energy entering ecosystems as sunlight is transferred by producers into chemical energy through photosynthesis and then from organism to organism through food webs.
Also covers: 5.c, 7.a, 7.g

Scan *Lesson 1 of your book. Write two facts you discovered about producers and consumers while scanning the lesson.*

1. _____

2. _____

Review Vocabulary **Define** ecosystem.

ecosystem _____

New Vocabulary *Use your book or a dictionary to define the following terms.*

ecology _____
_____

producer _____
_____

photosynthesis _____
_____

consumer _____
_____

decomposer _____
_____

Academic Vocabulary *Use a dictionary to define* structure.

structure _____
_____

Lesson 1 Producers and Consumers (continued)

◄ Main Idea ► _____ **◄ Details ►**

Ecosystems

I found this information on page _____.

Classify *factors in a pond ecosystem as* biotic *or* abiotic. *Include at least six factors.*

Factors of a Pond Ecosystem	
Biotic	Abiotic

I found this information on page _____.

Summarize *the key relationship between the biotic factors and the abiotic factors in an ecosystem.*

_____

_____

Producers

I found this information on page _____.

Sequence *the steps by which* plants make and use food.

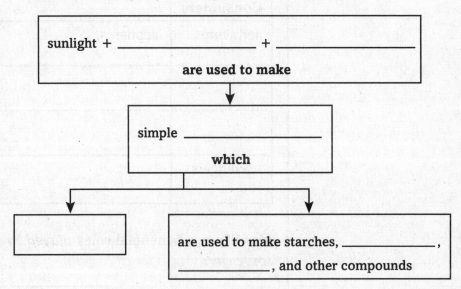

sunlight + _____ + _____

are used to make

↓

simple _____

which

are used to make starches, _____,

_____, and other compounds

┌─────────────────────────────┐
│ **SUMMARIZE IT** │
└─────────────────────────────┘
Summarize three main ideas of the above sections.

_____

_____

_____

Main Idea

Details

Producers

I found this information on page _____.

Compare and contrast photosynthesis *with* chemosynthesis. *Identify the energy source for each and list organisms that use each.*

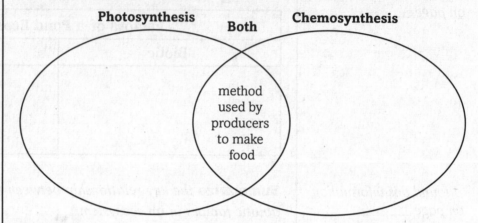

Consumers

I found this information on page _____.

Distinguish *between the* types of consumers. *Give at least two examples of each type of consumer and identify what they eat.*

Types of Consumers	Examples	What They Eat
herbivores	elephants,	plants
scavengers		

Identify *two* beneficial roles *played by decomposers and* scavengers.

Decomposers

SUMMARIZE IT

Highlight the main idea in the information below.

Consumers are categorized by the kinds of foods they eat. For example, lions are categorized as carnivores because they eat meat, and bears are omnivores because they eat both animals and plants.

Energy and Matter in Ecosystems
Lesson 2 Energy in Ecosystems

 Grade 6 Science Content Standards—5.a: Students know energy entering ecosystems as sunlight is transferred by producers into chemical energy through photosynthesis and then from organism to organism through food webs. Also covers: 5.b, 5.c, 7.b, 7.d, 7.e

Scan *the headings in Lesson 2 of your book. Predict three things you will learn.*

1. _____

2. _____

3. _____

New Vocabulary *Read the definitions below. Write the correct vocabulary term on the blank to the left of each definition.*

_____ consumer at the top of the energy pyramid

_____ complicated model of the flow of energy in an ecosystem

_____ consumer at the bottom of the energy pyramid

_____ illustration of how energy moves through an ecosystem

_____ consumer at the second level of the energy pyramid

Academic Vocabulary *Use a dictionary to define the term* convert *as it is used in the following sentence.*

Producers such as trees and bushes convert sunlight, water, and carbon dioxide into sugars.

convert _____

_____

Lesson 2 Energy in Ecosystems (continued)

<table>
<tr><td>**Main Idea**</td><td>**Details**</td></tr>
</table>

Energy Through the Ecosystem

I found this information on page _____.

Sequence the flow of energy through ecosystems. *Fill in the boxes with the words* producers, consumers, *and* decomposers.

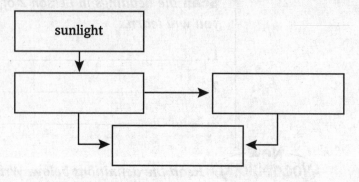

sunlight

Food as Energy

I found this information on page _____.

Create *an example of a* food chain.

- *Include and label a* producer, *a* herbivore, *and a* carnivore *or* omnivore *that eats the herbivore.*

- *Use arrows to show* the transfer of energy.

I found this information on page _____.

Rephrase *in your own words why a* food web *is a more accurate model of energy flow through an ecosystem than a food chain.*

_____

_____

_____

_____

SUMMARIZE IT

Summarize the two main ideas of this section.

_____

_____

Lesson 2 Energy in Ecosystems (continued)

Main Idea	Details

Food as Energy

I found this information on page _____.

Draw *arrows to show how energy would flow in this food web.*

foxes

snakes

lizards

desert plants

insects

I found this information on page _____.

Identify *an example of an organism at each level of the* energy pyramid.

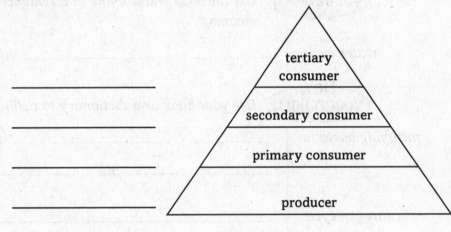

tertiary consumer

secondary consumer

primary consumer

producer

_____

_____

_____

_____

I found this information on page _____.

Analyze *why a pyramid is used as the model for energy flow through an ecosystem.*

_____

_____

_____

_____

SUMMARIZE IT Write two sentences to summarize the above section.

_____

_____

_____

Energy and Matter in Ecosystems
Lesson 3 Matter in Ecosystems

 Grade 6 Science Content Standards—5.b: Students know matter is transferred over time from one organism to others in the food web and between organisms and the physical environment. Also covers: 7.a, 7.b, 7.g

Skim *the headings and illustrations of Lesson 3 to identify four cycles that will be discussed.*

1. _____

2. _____

3. _____

4. _____

Review Vocabulary

Use the term **water cycle** *in a sentence to show its scientific meaning.*

water cycle _____

New Vocabulary

Use your book or a dictionary to define the following terms.

nitrifying bacteria _____

_____

nitrogen cycle _____

_____

phosphorus cycle _____

_____

carbon cycle _____

_____

Academic Vocabulary

Use the word **resource** *in a scientific sentence.*

resource _____

_____

Lesson 3 Matter in Ecosystems (continued)

‹Main Idea› _____ **‹Details›**

Cycles of Matter

I found this information on page _____.

Summarize *how dead plant and animal material are made available to support new life.*

_____

_____

_____

_____

Water Cycle

I found this information on page _____.

Sequence the main steps in the water cycle.

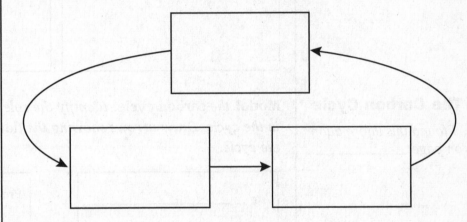

I found this information on page _____.

Model *the nitrogen cycle in a diagram.*

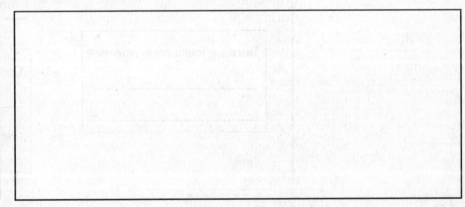

SUMMARIZE IT Summarize two main ideas of the above section with bullet points.

_____

_____

Lesson 3 **Matter in Ecosystems** (continued)

⟨ **Main Idea** ⟩ _____ ⟨ **Details** ⟩

Phosphorous Cycle

I found this information on page _____.

Compare and contrast *the* phosphorus cycle *with the* nitrogen cycle.

Unlike nitrogen, phosphorus:	Like nitrogen, phosphorus:

The Carbon Cycle

I found this information on page _____.

Model *the* carbon cycle. *Identify the role of each item shown in the cycle. Draw arrows showing the flow of carbon through the cycle.*

Air _____
_____ .

Producers (plants and algae)

use _____ to

make _____ .

Burning fossil fuels releases

_____

_____ .

Consumers break down

_____ and

release _____

_____ .

SUMMARIZE IT

Summarize the main idea of the above section.

_____

_____

_____

Tie It Together

Synthesize It

Create a food web.

1. Make a list of foods that you ate yesterday.
2. Determine whether the main component of each food came from a producer or a consumer.
3. For each consumer, identify at least one food that it ate.
4. Create a food web that includes yourself.

List:

Web:

Energy and Matter in Ecosystems
Chapter Wrap-Up

Now that you have read the chapter, think about what you have learned and complete the table below. Compare your previous answers to these.

1. Write an **A** if you agree with the statement.
2. Write a **D** if you disagree with the statement.

Energy and Matter in Ecosystems	After You Read
• An ecosystem is made up of both living and nonliving things.	
• Plants make their own food.	
• Energy cycles through ecosystems.	
• All living things release some food energy as heat.	

Review
Use this checklist to help you study.

- [ ] Review the information you included in your Foldable.
- [ ] Study your *Science Notebook* on this chapter.
- [ ] Study the definitions of vocabulary words.
- [ ] Review daily homework assignments.
- [ ] Re-read the chapter and review the charts, graphs, and illustrations.
- [ ] Review the Standards Check at the end of each lesson.
- [ ] Look over the Standards Review at the end of the chapter.

SUMMARIZE IT After reading this chapter, write one summary sentence for each lesson to explain the chapter's main ideas.

_____
_____
_____
_____

Resources

 Grade 6 Science Content Standards—6.a: Students know the utility of energy sources is determined by factors that are involved in converting these sources to useful forms and the consequences of the conversion process. Also covers: 6.b, 6.c, 7.b–e

Before You Read

Before you read the chapter, respond to these statements.

1. Write an **A** if you agree with the statement.
2. Write a **D** if you disagree with the statement.

Before You Read	Resources
	• Gold is a nonrenewable mineral resource.
	• The supply of fossil fuels is unlimited.
	• Sun and wind are nonpolluting alternative energy resources.
	• Oil is used to make plastic and nylon.

 *Construct the Foldable as directed at the beginning of this chapter.*

Science Journal

Look around your classroom or your bedroom at home. Make a list of the objects that are made from resources in nature.

_____

_____

_____

_____

_____

_____

Name _____   Date _____

Resources
Lesson 1 Earth's Material Resources

 Grade 6 Science Content Standards—6.b: Students know different natural energy and material resources, including air, soil, rocks, minerals, petroleum, fresh water, wildlife, and forests, and know how to classify them as renewable or nonrenewable. Also covers: 6.c, 7.c

Skim *Lesson 1 of your book. Predict three topics that might be discussed.*

1. _____

2. _____

3. _____

Review Vocabulary

Define magma.

magma

_____

_____

New Vocabulary

Use your book or a dictionary to define the following terms.

natural resource

_____

_____

renewable natural resource

_____

_____

estuary

_____

_____

nonrenewable natural resource

_____

_____

Academic Vocabulary

Use a dictionary to define regulate. *Then use it in a sentence to show its meaning.*

regulate

_____

_____

Name _____ Date _____

Lesson 1 Earth's Material Resources (continued)

Main Idea   **Details**

Organic Resources

I found this information on page _____ .

Define organic material resources, *and give five examples of these resources.*

Organic material resources are _____

_____

Examples: _____

Inorganic Resources

I found this information on page _____ .

Organize *information about* inorganic resources. *Complete the concept map with examples.*

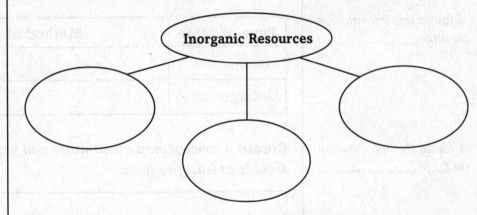

Renewable Resources

I found this information on page _____ .

Identify *four reasons that* forests are important.

Forests

┌─────────────────────────────────────┐
│ **SUMMARIZE IT**   │
└─────────────────────────────────────┘
Summarize two main ideas of the above sections.

_____

_____

_____

_____

Lesson 1 Earth's Material Resources (continued)

Main Idea   ## Details

Renewable Resources

I found this information on page _____.

Analyze *how human activity affects* estuaries *and other wetlands.* *Complete the cause-and-effect diagram.*

| Humans use wetland areas in ways that destroy _____. | → | |

Nonrenewable Resources

I found this information on page _____.

Compare and contrast *the different ways through which gold can be extracted from Earth.*

Type of Mine	Method of Extraction
Placer	
Underground	

I found this information on page _____.

Create *a concept map about water and water use in California.* *Include at least five facts.*

SUMMARIZE IT

Summarize three main ideas of the above sections.

_____

_____

_____

Resources
Lesson 2 Energy Resources

 Grade 6 Science Content Standards—6.a: Students know the utility of energy sources is determined by factors that are involved in converting these sources to useful forms and the consequences of the conversion process. Also covers: 6.b, 7.b, 7.e

Scan *Lesson 2 of your book. Use the checklist below.*

☐ Read all of the headings.

☐ Read all of the boldface words.

☐ Look at the tables and figures.

☐ Think about what you already know about energy resources.

Write three things that you predict will be covered in the lesson.

1. _____

2. _____

3. _____

Review Vocabulary **Define** crust.

crust

_____

_____

New Vocabulary *Read the definitions below. Write the correct vocabulary term on the blank to the left of each definition.*

_____ heat energy in Earth's crust

_____ joining of two atoms to form a different atom

_____ fuel formed in Earth's crust over hundreds of millions of years

_____ splitting atoms to release energy

Academic Vocabulary *Use a dictionary to define* technology. *Then use it in a sentence to show its scientific meaning.*

technology

_____

_____

_____

Lesson 2 Energy Resources (continued)

Main Idea   **Details**

Fossil Fuels

*I found this information
on page _____.*

Compare and contrast oil *and* natural gas *by completing the
Venn diagram below with at least seven facts.*

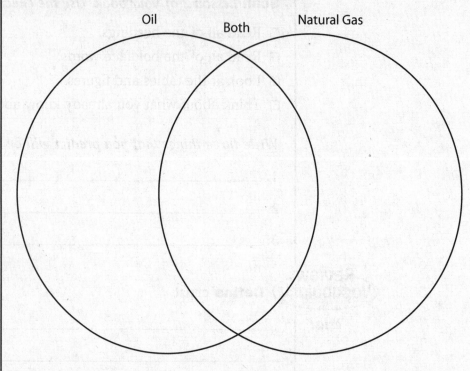

Oil   Both   Natural Gas

Formation of Fossil Fuels

*I found this information
on page _____.*

Sequence *the 5 steps in the formation of* coal.

1.	
2.	
3.	
4.	
5.	

SUMMARIZE IT
Summarize the main ideas of this lesson.

_____

_____

_____

_____

Lesson 2 Energy Resources (continued)

◁ **Main Idea** ▷ _____ ◁ **Details** ▷ _____

Alternatives to Fossil Fuels and **Energy from Resources**

I found this information on page _____.

Organize *information about* alternative energy sources.

Type of Energy	How It Works	Advantages	Disadvantages
Hydro-electric	Water moves through a dam to generate electricity.	renewable	requires dams to be built
Wind			
Geo-thermal			
Nuclear			
Solar			
Biomass			
Wave			

SUMMARIZE IT Summarize the main idea of the above section.

_____

_____

_____

Resources
Lesson 3 Using Energy and Material Resources

 Grade 6 Science Content Standards—6.a: Students know the utility of energy sources is determined by factors that are involved in converting these sources to useful forms and the consequences of the conversion process. Also covers: 6.b, 6.c, 7.a, 7.d, 7.e

Skim *Lesson 3 of your book. Write three questions that come to mind. Look for answers to your questions as you read the lesson.*

1. _____

2. _____

3. _____

Review Vocabulary **Define** global warming.

global warming _____

_____

New Vocabulary *Use your book to define the following terms. Then write a sentence that uses two of the terms together.*

conservation _____

_____

recycling _____

_____

particulate _____

_____

Sentence: _____

Academic Vocabulary *Use a dictionary to define* register *as a verb. Then use it in a sentence to show its scientific meaning.*

register _____

_____

Lesson 3 Using Energy and Material Resources (continued)

⟨ **Main Idea** ⟩ _____   ⟨ **Details** ⟩ _____

Location of Natural Resources

I found this information on page _____ .

Label *the map below to show where resources are located in the United States. Choose five resources, and locate them on the map. Use colors and/or symbols to show where each resource is located, and make a legend for your map in the left margin.*

Manufacturing Common Objects

I found this information on page _____ .

Complete *the table to identify materials used to* manufacture *common objects.*

Object	Plastic	Chemical	Pencil
Resource(s)			

Summarize *what* recycling *is and why it is important.*

_____
_____
_____

SUMMARIZE IT

Summarize the main ideas of the above sections with two bullet points.

_____
_____
_____

Lesson 3 Using Energy and Material Resources (continued)

Main Idea

Drawbacks of Using Fossil Fuel

I found this information on page _____.

Details

Identify *and describe damage caused by pollutants produced by fossil fuels.*

Pollutant	Damaging Effects
Oil spills	
Carbon dioxide	
	forms acid rain
	creates smog in urban areas
Particulates	

I found this information on page _____.

Identify *six ways to conserve gasoline.*

1. _____
2. _____
3. _____
4. _____
5. _____
6. _____

SUMMARIZE IT

Summarize two main ideas of the above sections.

_____
_____
_____

Name _____ Date _____

Lesson 3 Using Energy and Material Resources (continued)

Main Idea	Details

Alternative Energy and the Environment

I found this information on page _____.

Classify *types of* alternative energy *and their effects on the environment.*

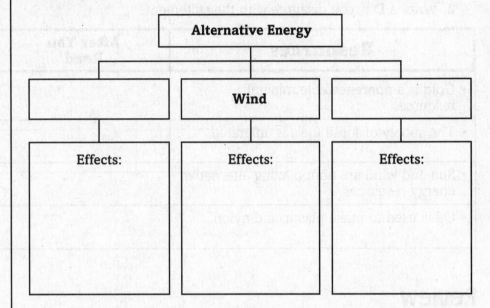

Using Energy Resources Wisely

I found this information on page _____.

Analyze *what will happen if* nonrenewable energy *resources are used at current levels over time. Complete the cause-and-effect diagram.*

> Nonrenewable resources continue to be used at current levels.

Define conservation, *and explain why it is useful.*

_____

_____

_____

SUMMARIZE IT

Summarize the main ideas of the above sections with two bullet points.

_____

_____

Resources Chapter Wrap-Up

Now that you have read the chapter, think about what you have learned and complete the table below. Compare your previous answers to these.

1. Write an **A** if you agree with the statement.
2. Write a **D** if you disagree with the statement.

Resources	After You Read
• Gold is a nonrenewable mineral resource.	
• The supply of fossil fuels is unlimited.	
• Sun and wind are nonpolluting alternative energy resources.	
• Oil is used to make plastic and nylon.	

Review

Use this checklist to help you study.

☐ Review the information you included in your Foldable.

☐ Study your *Science Notebook* on this chapter.

☐ Study the definitions of vocabulary words.

☐ Review daily homework assignments.

☐ Re-read the chapter and review the charts, graphs, and illustrations.

☐ Review the Standards Check at the end of each lesson.

☐ Look over the Standards Review at the end of the chapter.

SUMMARIZE IT After studying the chapter, write one or two sentences to summarize the main idea of each lesson.

_____

_____

_____

_____